D1314118

PRENTICE HALL
Choices
in LITERATURE

The Adventure of Me
Joining Hands
It's Up to You
Conflict and Resolution
The World of "What if . . . ?"

The Me You See
Where Paths Meet
Deciding What's Right
You Are the Solution
Communication Explosion

Myself, My World
American Tapestry
Justice for All
Making a Difference
Charting Your Own Course

Master Teacher Board

Elizabeth Ferreira-Alves
Magnet Lead Teacher
Mays Middle School
Miami, Florida

Sarah Bennett
Chairperson, English Department
Martin Luther King/Law and Public Service
  High School
Cleveland, Ohio

Erick Carter
Teacher 9–12
Marjory Stoneman Douglas High School
Parkland, Florida

Beverly Ann Chin
Professor of English
Director of Montana Writing Project
University of Montana
Missoula, Montana

Anita L. Clay
District Coordinator
Gateway Institute of Technology
Saint Louis, Missouri

Terri Fields
Teacher 9–12
Sunnyslope High School
Phoenix, Arizona

Lynn Gallardo
Title I/SIP Facilitator
Irvine Intermediate School
Garden Grove, California

Margaret Honey
Associate Center Director
Center for Children and Educational Technology
Bank Street College
New York, New York

Jennifer Huntress
Secondary Language Arts Coordinator
Putnam City Schools
Oklahoma City, Oklahoma

James Lynch
Department Supervisor for English 6–12
Canandaigua Academy
Canandaigua, New York

Donna Miller
Program Specialist for English (Retired)
Orange County Public Schools
Orlando, Florida

Ann Okamura
Teacher 9–12
Laguna Creek High School
Elk Grove, California

Dr. Sylvia Rendón
Coordinator for Humanities
Tomball Integrated School District
Tomball, Texas

Terry Ross
District Secondary Language Arts Coordinator
Round Rock Independent School District
Round Rock, Texas

John Scott
English Instructor
Hampton High School
Hampton, Virginia

William Wright
Executive Director
Consortium for School Networking (CoSN)
Washington, D.C.

Program Advisor

Dr. Lisbeth Ceaser
Literacy and Teacher Education Consultant
California Polytechnic State University
San Luis Obispo, California

The Student Review Board is listed on
pages K146–148.

Contributing Writers

Joseph Bruchac
Storyteller and Writer
Greenfield Center, New York

Marie G. Lee
Novelist
New York, New York

Diane Tasca
Former English Instructor
University of Illinois
Urbana, Illinois

William Winfield
Poet and Editor
New York, New York

PRENTICE HALL
Choices
in LITERATURE

Myself, My World

PRENTICE HALL
Upper Saddle River, New Jersey
Needham, Massachusetts

Copyright © 1997 by Prentice-Hall, Inc., a Viacom Company, Upper Saddle River, New Jersey 07458. All rights reserved. No part of this book may be reproduced or transmitted in any form or by any means, electronic or mechanical, including photocopying, recording, or by any information storage or retrieval system, without permission in writing from the publisher. Printed in the United States of America.

ISBN 0-13-411620-8

1 2 3 4 5 6 7 8 9 10   00 99 98 97 96

Cover: Student Art *Untitled,* Che Chen, Walt Whitman High School, Bethesda, Maryland

Art credits begin on page K149.

PRENTICE HALL
Simon & Schuster Education Group
A VIACOM COMPANY

Staff Credits for Prentice Hall Choices in Literature

(In Alphabetical Order)

Advertising and Promotion: Carol Leslie, Alfonso Manosalvas, Rip Odell

Business Office: Emily Heins

Design: Eric Dawson, Jim O'Shea, Carol Richman, AnnMarie Roselli, Gerry Schrenk

Editorial: Ellen Bowler, Megan Chill, Barbara W. Coe, Elisa Mui Eiger, Philip Fried, Rebecca Z. Graziano, Douglas McCollum

Manufacturing and Inventory Planning: Katherine Clarke, Rhett Conklin, Matt McCabe

Marketing: Jean Faillace, Mollie Ledwith

Media Resources: Libby Forsyth, Maureen Raymond

National Language Arts Consultants: Kathy Lewis, Karen Massey, Craig A. McGhee, Vennisa Travers, Gail Witt

Permissions: Doris Robinson

Pre-press Production: Carol Barbara, Kathryn Dix, Marie McNamara, Annette Simmons

Production: Margaret Antonini, Christina Burghard, Greg Myers, Marilyn Stearns, Cleasta Wilburn

Sales: Ellen Backstrom

Acknowledgments

Grateful acknowledgment is made to the following for permission to reprint copyrighted material:

Airmount Publishing Company
"I Learn to Speak" from *The Story of My Life* by Helen Keller. Published by Airmount Publishing Company, Inc., 1965.

Camille Andrews
"Lanterns" by Camille Andrews, published in *Virginia Writing,* Volume 7, No. 2, © Longwood College 1993. Reprinted by permission of the author.

Arte Publico Press–University of Houston
"This Morning There Were Rainbows in the Sprinklers" by Lorna Dee Cervantes is reprinted with permission from the publisher of *Hispanic, Female and Young: An Anthology,* edited by Phyllis Tashlik (Houston: Arte Publico Press–University of Houston, 1994). "Maestro" by Pat Mora is reprinted with permission from the publisher of *Chants* (Houston: Arte Publico Press–University of Houston, 1986).

Toni Cade Bambara
"Raymond's Run" is reprinted with permission of the author. Copyright © 1971 by Toni Cade Bambara. Story appears in Bambara collection *Gorilla, My Love.*

(Continued on page K149.)

Myself, My World
Contents

Looking at Literary Forms: The Short Story

HOW DO I RELATE TO OTHERS?

Looking at Literary Forms: Poetry

HOW DO I SHAPE MY WORLD?

About This Program

What makes reading exciting?

Reading is a great way to learn more about the world and about yourself. Reading gives you the chance to make a movie in your mind and experience adventures you might never be able to actually live. Words can take you to faraway lands, tell you about important discoveries and courageous people, make you laugh and cry, or let you look at your world in a new way.

How will reading pay off in your future?

Beyond being entertaining, reading is important. As you learn more, you increase your choices in life. The skills and strategies you practice today will help you to become a life-long learner—someone who has questions, reads to answer them, and develops more questions!

How will this book help you get more out of what you read?

This book and your teacher will help you become a better reader. The selections included will grab your attention and help you practice specific skills valuable to the reading process.

Questions and activities at the beginning of selections will help you relate the reading to your own life; questions at the end will help you expand on what you learned. Activities and projects throughout the book will help you generate and explore new pathways of learning.

What features make this book a great learning tool?

• **Artwork to Spark Your Interest** Fine art, student art, photography, and maps can give you clues about the writing and direct the way you read.

• **Exciting Activities to Get You Into the Selection** A preview page for each selection asks a question to get you thinking. Stop and consider your own responses to this question. Talk with classmates to get their ideas. As you read, you may find your own opinions changing. Reading can do that, too.

 The **Reach Into Your Background** feature will always give you ideas for connecting the selection to your own experience. In many cases, you may know more than you think you do. Try the activities in this section for a jump start before you read. Don't expect to be in your seats all the time! You'll learn more about your ideas by role-playing, debating, and sharing what you know with others.

• **Useful Strategies to Help You Through the Selection** This program will teach you essential techniques for getting more out of your reading.

In **Read Actively** you'll find hands-on approaches to getting more out of what you read. Here's your chance to practice the skills that will bring you reading success. You'll learn to make inferences, gather evidence, set a purpose for reading, and much more. Once you've learned these skills, you can use them in all the reading that you do . . . and you'll get more out of your reading.

Some of the strategies you'll learn include:

Identifying Problems

Making Judgments

Asking Questions

Visualizing Characters

Setting a Purpose for Reading

Recognizing a Sequence of Events

Connecting Nonfiction to Your Own Experience

Responding to Literature

· Thought-Provoking Activities to Generate New Ideas Following each selection, you'll have the chance to explore your own ideas and learn more about what you read.

Explore Your Reading takes you into, through, and beyond the actual selection to help you investigate the writing and its ideas more closely.

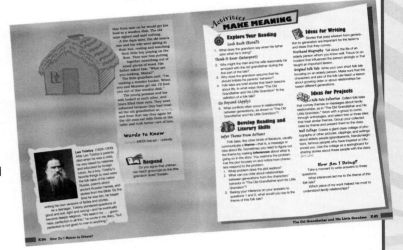

Develop Reading and Literary Skills expands your knowledge of literary forms, terms, and techniques. Following up on the Read Actively activities and strategies, you will learn more about how writing communicates.

Ideas for Writing and **Ideas for Projects** offer you the chance to create your own answers to your own questions. How does the selection relate to you? Where can you learn more? What cross-curricular connections can you make? These ideas features help you try things out yourself.

Enjoy this book!

All the features of this program fit together to develop your interest, skills, and, ultimately, your ability to learn.

Have fun with the time you spend with this book. Look at the art, plan for unit level projects, look for connections between selections. Pay attention to your own questions—finding the answers to those may be the most rewarding of all.

Myself, My World

Untitled Alexandra Maldonado, SIS, New York City

"My life belongs to the world.
I will do what I can." —James Dickey

Get the Picture

Look at the picture of the Earth surrounded by people. What does it say about your world? Think about what James Dickey says about his life belonging to the world. Do you feel the same way? What can you do to shape the world around you?

These questions are the focus of this unit:

• How Do I Express Myself?
• How Do I Relate to Others?
• How Do I Shape My World?

The authors in this unit have asked themselves questions like these, and their answers will help you sort out your own thinking. As you explore the unit, you can use your journal to add your own questions, to answer them, and to consider how your reading can help you shape your world.

Activities

In a Group Discuss how the world has shaped your lives so far, and predict how it may shape your lives in the future. First, identify two world events that have influenced you and describe how they have affected your outlook. Then list two trends that you think will affect your future, and describe the effects they may have on your generation. Create a poster that highlights the features you have identified.

Activities

On Your Own Make a two-column self-assessment table. Use the headings "Contributions I've Made" and "Contributions I Can Make." First list the ways in which you have already contributed to the world. Then predict the ways in which you can contribute to the world in the future. Consider your own special talents and interests.

Project Preview . . . .

You can also respond to these questions by working on challenging projects. Preview the following projects and choose the ones you might like to do. For more details, see pages K130–K131.

- **Self-Portrait**
- **Class Anthology**
- **Storytelling Festival**

- **Career Day**
- **Hometown Celebration**
- **School of the Future**

Read Actively

How does my reading relate to my world?

How can I get more from what I read?

The answer to questions like these is to be an active reader, an *involved* reader. As an active reader, you are in charge of the reading situation!

The following strategies tell how to think as an active reader. You don't need to use all of these strategies all of the time. Feel free to choose the ones that work best in each reading situation.

BEFORE YOU READ

PREVIEW
What do the title and the pictures suggest? What will the selection say about "Myself, My World"?

GIVE YOURSELF A PURPOSE
What is the author communicating?
What will you learn about the theme?
How will the selection relate to your life?

REACH INTO YOUR BACKGROUND
What do you know already?

WHiLE YOU READ

AFTER YOU READ

PREDICT

What do you think will happen? Why? You can change your mind as you read along.

ASK QUESTIONS

What's happening? Why do the characters do what they do? Why does the author give you certain details or use a particular word? Your questions help you gather evidence and make inferences.

VISUALIZE

What would these events and characters look like in a movie? How would the writer's descriptions look in a photograph?

CONNECT

Are characters like you or someone you know? What would you do in a similar situation?

RESPOND

Talk about what you've read. What did you think?

ASSESS YOURSELF

How did you do? Were your predictions on target? Did you find answers to your questions?

FOLLOW UP

Show what you know. Get involved! Do a project. Keep learning.

The model that begins on the next page shows Nicole Frosh's thoughts while actively reading "Calling Jack Kettle."

I'm thirteen years old and an 8th-grade honor student at Columbia Middle School in Aurora, Colorado, where I live with my Mom and Dad, baby sister, and pets. I'm active in soccer, swimming, cycling, Odyssey of the Mind, advanced math, peer tutoring, and peer counseling. I believe that active reading is the key to all successful reading.

Nicole Frosh

This title makes me wonder: Who is Jack Kettle? Who is calling Jack Kettle? What does the word "calling" mean here? [Ask questions]

Calling Jack Kettle

Norma Fox Mazer

Meadow wanted to call Jack Kettle. That is, she wanted Jessie to call, but not say who she was or who she was calling for. Meadow had seen him behind the counter one day at the clubhouse. She hadn't stopped talking about him since. How good looking he was. What a sweet smile. What a great build.

"Etcetera, etcetera," Jessie broke in. They were upstairs in Meadow's room. I'm past the stage of making anonymous calls to boys. You should be too, Med."

This conversation gives me background knowledge about the characters. I can understand their relationship. [Background]

"Jessie!" Meadow's little pale face flamed. "You know how I am."

"Shy," Jessie sighed.

"*Massively* shy."

"What if you just talk to him at the clubhouse?" Jessie asked.

"Do *what*?" Meadow sounded as shocked as if Jessie had recommended she commit an unmentionable act.

"What if I make the call, but you talk to him?"

"Jessie—"

"What if I get things started, then hand you the phone?" She didn't even wait for Meadow's protest. She just dialed his number. Why not? She'd been speaking for Meadow ever since they became best friends, way back in kindergarten.

"Hello?"

"Jack Kettle, please," Jessie said.

By looking at the pictures in the story, I predict the story will involve teenagers. [Predict]

"Speaking."

"Ahh, Jack . . ." Jessie cleared her throat and dropped her voice to what she hoped was a low, fascinating drawl. "How fortunate I found you in. I have a message for you. Someone I know thinks you are *très* interesting."

"You mean you?"

"If I meant myself, Jack, I would say so."

Words to Know

unmentionable (un MEN shun uh buhl) *adj*: Not fit for polite conversation

Untitled, Susan Kahn
Collection of the Montclair Art Museum

What do the characters look like? [Ask questions]

He laughed. "You sound cute."

Meadow was breathing warmly on Jessie's neck. "Jack," Jessie said. "Believe me, I'm not your type."

"This other girl, is she pretty?"

"Is that all that matters to you guys? However, if you must know, yes, she's pretty. Blonde, with big brown eyes, plus she's smart and athletic. Plus, she has an adorable mole near her mouth."

"Ssss." Meadow dug her chin warningly into Jessie's shoulder.

"She's blonde?"

Jessie sighed. Didn't he hear anything else she'd said? "Why do you boys always get excited about blondes?"

He laughed again. "I don't know. What's her name?"

"Now, now, Jack. That's a secret. I'll give you a hint, her first initial is M."

"Marylee Farber?"

"Don't you wish." Marylee was a senior who had

been prom queen last year and who was a shoo-in for valedictorian this year.

"Melody Farmer?"

"No, Jack."

"Misty Alzicia? Margaret—"

"Wrong, wrong, wrong again. Bye, bye. No more guesses."

Jessie put the phone down.

"You told him about my mole." Meadow touched the corner of her mouth. "He's going to know who I am."

"Is that the thanks I get for doing your dog work?"

"What do you want me to do?"

"Grovel at my feet . . . Say I'm a wonderful friend."

"You're a wonderful friend."

Jessie smiled modestly. "I know."

The next time they called Jack Kettle, they were in Jessie's house. A woman answered the phone. "Could I speak to Jack, please?" Jessie said.

"Who's calling?"

"Aaah, a friend."

"Just a moment . . . Jack!"

"Jessie, was that his mother?"

"I think so, Meadow."

"How did she sound?"

"Like a mother, Meadow."

"Hello?" Jack said.

"Jack! This is your mystery friend, speaking on behalf of MBC, or should I say the fabulous MBC."

"Is that for Most Beautiful Creature?"

"Very good, Jack!"

"What school do you go to?"

"Me to know, you to wonder, Jack. You know nothing about me, and that's the way it should be. I, however, know what you look like, where you work, and—"

"You're giving him too many clues."

"When am I going to meet you in person?" he said. "You sound so cute. And your voice! Good voice!"

"Did you ever hear a bad voice? Don't bother answering. I am not cute. And now, you're thinking, If she's not cute, why am I talking to her?"

> This reminds me of some of the crazy things that my friends and I do. These characters seem like real teenagers. [Connect]

> Jessie and Meadow remind me of my friends and the way we concern ourselves with boys and occasionally fall for the same guy. [Connect]

Words to Know

valedictorian (val uh dik TOR ee uhn) *n.*: Highest-ranking student in a class

grovel (GRUHV uhl) *v.*: Behave very humbly

"I'm not thinking that!"

"Sure you are. Goodbye, I'm tired of talking to you."

"Why did you hang up on him, Jessie?"

"Because I felt like it, Meadow. He was boring me. Why are we whispering?"

The third call to Jack Kettle was from a phone booth in front of a gas station on Nottingham Road. "I wouldn't do this for anyone but you," Jessie said.

"I know." Meadow put her guitar case down.

"Prepare for disappointment," Jessie added instructively. "He was home the first two times, he won't be home this time. Law of averages, Meadow."

Jack Kettle answered on the first ring.

"Law of averages, Meadow," Meadow mouthed at Jessie.

"Hey, it's the girl with the voice," Jack Kettle said.

"Hey, it's the boy with the laugh."

He laughed.

"Did you ever think, Jack, that our planet is like a huge sprawling house, and we humans are like the family that moved in and forgot to pay the rent."

This is a fantastic question and metaphor! [Respond]

"Hey!"

"When the family moved in, they had more rooms than they would ever need. So they thought, Jack. Which is why they didn't bother cleaning up their messes. If a room got too grotty, they just shut the door and trekked on to a nice fresh room."

"Jessie, what are you doing?"

"A long time passed, Jack, and they started having trouble with the house. The plumbing wasn't the greatest anymore. The roof was leaking, and nearly every room was in use." She paused. "What do you think about all this, Jack?"

"He doesn't think anything," Meadow said. "He's gone." She had her finger pressed down on the switch. "*You* were boring *him*, Jessie." She picked up her guitar case and walked away.

"How do you know that?" Jessie said, going after her.

"Because you were boring me! Besides, there wasn't anything about me in that conversation."

"Meadow, I can't mention your name, I can't say how you look, I can't say that you know him from the Clubhouse. What am I supposed to say?"

"I don't know," Meadow said.

"Besides, he's a muscle-bound jerk. Why don't you get a crush on someone smart?"

"He's not a jerk!"

"All those guys with muscles are jerks."

"You make me so mad when you say stupid things like that!"

"And you make me mad when you say the things I say are stupid!"

They glared at each other. Then Meadow went one way, toward her guitar lesson, and Jessie went the other, toward the diner where her mother worked.

I can picture this scene: the girls would have their backs to each other, frowns on their faces, and their arms crossed against their chests. [Visualize]

In the morning, Jessie was in a bad mood. She always was when she and Meadow quarreled. The worst part about it was that today was the annual Save the County Walk. This was the third year Jessie had signed up and, grumpy as she felt, she still wasn't going to miss it. Her mother drove her to the park where the walk started.

Her team consisted of an older man with big square teeth, a couple wearing identical denim outfits, and a boy in baggy striped pants, wearing a camouflage hat pulled down over his eyes.

Jessie started filling up her garbage bag, darting at

every glimmer of glass and metal. There was something gratifying about doing this—the same feeling she had when she attacked her room following a long period of grunge.

The older people had drifted to the other side of the road. They were laughing and having a good time, while she and the boy hadn't said a word. After what seemed like about five hundred minutes of silence, she said to him, "I heard there're a couple hundred people on this walk."

"Uh huh."

"Just her luck to be stuck with a brilliant conversationalist. She picked up a slimy piece of plastic. "Two hundred out of a quarter of a million. You'd think a few more would want to save it."

He glanced at her and dipped into the flattened grass for some beer cans.

"This is my third year doing this," she said, trying again.

"Hey."

"And it always rains."

"Why?"

"It's a law," she said. "I thought everyone knew. Even though the sun is shining when the walk begins, it has to rain before it's over . . ."

He laughed. Well, that was an improvement.

"How about you?" she said. "How many years have you been going on this walk?"

"My first time."

"Congratulations." *For saying three words.*

He jumped down into the ditch and came up holding a large brown plastic ball with a spout.

"Mutated beach ball," Jessie guessed.

"Party ball. Beer ball. Holds two gallons." He flattened it with his heel.

"I don't admire people getting drunk. What's fun

I predict that this boy is Jack and Jessie will fall for him. [Predict]

about getting wasted, smashed, sloshed, and acting like a fool? I'm a tee totaler."

She felt his eyes on her as she rolled a tire toward the road and tagged it for the truck. He probably thought she was a fanatic. She probably was.

"Eight ten-thousandths of a percent," he said suddenly.

"What?"

"Two hundred people is eight ten-thousandths of one percent of a quarter of a million."

"You did that in your head?"

He blushed. "I'm going to study sanitary engineering. Math is useful."

She bent down to clean up some broken glass. He knelt down too, putting them nose to nose. Suddenly he said, "Some eyebrows you have!"

"They're mine."

"I didn't say I didn't like them."

They walked again. This time he started the conversation. "I have an idea that the earth is like a house with a lot of rooms. And humans are the family who live in the house."

Jessie stared at him, speechless for once.

"Do you realize we're using up all the clean rooms?"

"I think I do," she managed. She'd realized something else too. She was only surprised she hadn't figured it out sooner. "What a great idea, Jack," she said.

He actually jumped with surprise. "You know my name?"

"I guess I do." Oh, why torture him? "You work at the Clubhouse, don't you?"

"Did you see me working out on the machines?" he asked hopefully.

Jack uses Jessie's metaphor without knowing he is talking to the person he heard it from! [Observe]

Words to Know

gratifying (GRAHT i fī ing) *n.*: Giving pleasure or satisfaction

fanatic (fuh NAT ik) *n.*: One who is overly enthusiastic about something

Jessie raised one of the eyebrows that awed him. "Oh man. Watching hunks work out on machines is not one of my preferred pastimes."

"You're so cute. What's your name?"

"Jessie. Quick, what's yours? Never mind. Just testing." She closed the full garbage bag with a twisty and left it by the side of the road for the truck. "How did you come up with that idea about the earth being a house?"

I like Jessie's comical responses—they are very amusing. [Respond]

"Ahhhh . . . it's actually not my idea." He blushed again. "My ahh girlfriend's. That is, ah, this girl I talk to on the phone . . ."

Jessie snapped open a fresh plastic bag and just then, the truth was revealed to her. Jack Kettle was not just a bonzo bunch of bulging muscles. Well, he was, but he was more than that. He was also sweet, honest when put to the test, and shy. Definitely shy.

Oh, no. Not another shy person in her life.

I feel sorry for Jack, because he doesn't know what he is getting himself into. [Respond]

"Bad," Jessie mumbled. "Bad, very bad!" She had not only fallen for Meadow's crush, but agreed to meet him in the mall on Monday afternoon. When Meadow found out, she was going to die of heartbreak, and then she was going to kill Jessie.

"*2 girls, 1 boy*," Jessie wrote in her notebook. "Jessie. Meadow. Jack." She perked up for a moment, noticing that she and Jack shared the same first initials. So what? Meadow had seen him first. Jessie hadn't even liked him. So sure that all his brains had dripped out of his head and down into his puffy muscular arms.

2 girls, 1 boy, 1 big mouth, she thought gloomily. She flung herself down on her bed and considered her options. She could tell Meadow about Jack . . . or she could not tell Meadow about Jack.

Tell her. Bring her to the mall to meet him. Friendship is stronger than crushes.

That was a noble thought.

Jack would see Meadow and blush. She was so pretty. His face would turn that adorable bright pink. Meadow would gasp and disappear behind Jessie.

Then what?

Neither of them would say a word

Jessie could see Meadow's face doing a dance of indecision. Yes no yes no. She could see Jack struggling for words.

Two shy people—that would never work. *Don't tell. Meet him at the mall. Do nothing and have Jack to yourself.*

I know that the problems in this story are very real, because my friends are always telling about these types of concerns. [Connect]

A mean, selfish thought.

She held her head in her hands. It was all up to her. Power, power, power. She could make things happen any way she wanted them to.

2 girls, 1 boy. 2 crushes, 1 friendship.

She staggered to her feet and stared at herself in the mirror for a long time. She saw a girl with a best friend. She saw a girl with a big crush. She saw a girl who didn't want to give up either one.

Listlessly, she took her lip gloss and drew a house with two windows and in each window, a girl. She made their hands touch. Then, with a little more energy, she drew a boy floating in space outside the house. She put in some stars and the sun and the moon, too, while she was at it. She hoped lip gloss wasn't too hard to get off glass. She drew a heart around the boy. The girls were smiling and looking toward him. He was smiling too.

She stood back and studied her work of art. What else did it need? She considered making the boy into a heart balloon and giving each one of the girls a string to it. But, finally, she did nothing. The picture was fine just the way it was. Two girls, 1 boy.

I plan to learn from Jessie's and Meadow's problem: NEVER LET A CRUSH GET IN THE WAY OF TRUE FRIENDSHIP! [Follow up]

Respond

- Do you think Jessie has made a wise decision? Why or why not?
- What advice would you give to Meadow about Jack?

Words to Know

listlessly (LIST lis lee) *adv*: Wearily; without energy

Norma Fox Mazer (1931–) recalls herself as a teenager of thirteen: "I'm at an adult gathering, sitting well back in a big side-winged leather chair, feeling hidden, unseen, almost invisible. My favorite state. I can watch, think, observe. Maybe that's the exact moment when I come to the amazing conclusion that adults are just like us, the kids, only taller, louder, pushier. . . . Now I can make up stories about them, too, because now I understand."

Explore Your Reading

Look Back (Recall)

1. Why does Jessie speak on the phone to Jack?

Think It Over (Interpret)

2. What impression of herself does Jessie make in her phone conversations with Jack?
3. Why does Meadow depend on Jessie? How does Jessie feel about this?
4. What makes Jessie change her mind about Jack?

Go Beyond (Apply)

5. Do you think it's a good idea to make sacrifices for your friends, as Jessie does? Explain.

Develop Reading and Literary Skills

Analyze Character Behavior

Once you get to know a person, you know how you expect that person to act in a given situation. The same is true of **characters**—the people in a story. As you read about what they say or do in one situation, you get a sense of how they will behave in another. This pattern of consistent behavior is a measure of how well the writer has told the story.

To judge whether or not a character acts consistently, you need to compare his or her behavior in different situations. Analyze Jessie's behavior in this way:

1. List three quotations, actions, or scenes that show Jessie's behavior in different parts of the story.
2. Write a few sentences explaining whether or not Jessie's actions are consistent with one another.
3. State one action that is consistent with Jessie's behavior and one action that is not consistent.

Ideas for Writing

What if Jessie, Meadow, and Jack were all friends of yours and you had to offer advice about how to maintain their friendships?

Evaluation Evaluate Jessie's decision in light of her responsibilities as a friend both to Meadow and to Jack. Explain her choice, and indicate where you agree (or disagree) with her. If you think she could have made a better decision, explain what she should have done, and why.

New Viewpoint Imagine that you are Jack telling a friend about his meeting with Jessie at the Save the County Walk. Use the facts presented in the story, but focus on Jack's views of Jessie. Include any change his feelings went through from the moment he saw her to his asking her to meet him at the mall.

Ideas for Projects

Community Cleanup Jessie and Jack get acquainted at a community cleanup. Get together with a group of classmates to discover what your community or a nearby town is doing to clean up its environment. Plan two activities you can do to support this work. Prepare posters to enlist student participation in these activities. [Social Studies Link]

Relationship Design Design a picture of the relationship among Jessie, Meadow, and Jack. Include in your design images that express your view of their connections (for example, a telephone). [Art Link]

How Am I Doing?

In your journal, jot down your responses to these questions:

What have I learned about analyzing the actions of characters?

How do I know when a character's behavior is consistent?

How Do I Express Myself?

Student Art *G-Clef: The Music and Me*
Michael Schwikardt, Cranford High School
Cranford, New Jersey

Untitled
Student Writing Christopher Thomas
Community School District 3, New York, New York

strings, wind, the sound of a symphony
gives me a feeling that I could be
a guitarist, a pianist, a person who plays
the
clarinet

saxophones, flutes together with a drum
set
they all are elements of my favorite sound
JAZZ JAZZ
that's all I hear now.

Voice   by Gabriel Olvera
This Morning There Were Rainbows in the Sprinklers
by Lorna Dee Cervantes

Has being in a particular place ever made your mood brighter—or darker?

Bear Lake, 1931 Georgia O'Keeffe, Museum of Fine Arts, Museum of New Mexico Foundation Collection

Reach Into Your Background

Have you noticed how movies use weather to express the mood or emotion of a scene? For example, a bright, sunny day forms the backdrop for a happy, carefree scene, while dark storm clouds and wind evoke mystery and danger. In a poem, the specific images set up or create the feelings and mood.

- With a partner, brainstorm to compile a list of places and images that you associate with a specific mood or feeling.
- Play charades: Take turns acting out (without words) a feeling or mood for others to identify.

Read Actively
Identify Speakers

The thoughts and emotions expressed in a poem tell you something about the poem's **speaker**. Like the narrator of a novel or a story, the speaker is the character who tells the poem and creates much of the poem's meaning. Identifying a poem's speaker and considering the speaker's outlook will help you better understand the poem.

As you read these poems, form a mental picture of the speaker in each. What are the thoughts, feelings or moods, and attitudes of each speaker? List the words or phrases that capture each speaker's personality.

VOICE

Gabriel Olvera

At school my voice is a plain
the soil of northern terrain
a great field of monotone days
flatland from October to May.

5 At home it is a row of hills
a southern sierra regaining color
or a Mexican range come every summer
my voice from June to September.

Respond

In this poem, the speaker creates two completely different images of his life. Which image appeals to you most? Why?

Gabriel Olvera grew up in downtown Los Angeles but studied in the San Francisco Bay area. The images in his poem "Voice" may come from his experiences with the sixth-graders he teaches in the San Fernando Valley of southern California.

Words to Know

terrain (te RAYN) *n.*: An area of land (line 2)
monotone (MAHN uh tohn) *adj.*: A single color; a flat, unvaried sound (line 3)
sierra (see AYR uh) *n.*: Mountain range (line 6)

This Morning There Were Rainbows in the Sprinklers

— Lorna Dee Cervantes

This morning
there were rainbows in the sprinklers.
My hollow heels clopped as they wore away the pavement
Clop, clop, clop.
5 I sang a worn out folk song
to the steady clop of my heels
wearing out the song
along with my heels
along with the pavement.
10 I was glad
because I wasn't sleepy anymore
but I yawned
more out of habit than out of sleepiness.
Today it's spring
15 and the remnants of April crush against my skin
in the wind.
It feels good.
The sky is clear
and I can see last night's quarter moon
20 like it was etched in the sky with cloud dust.
I time out my song to end
just as I reach my destiny.
I feel like I'm in a movie
a musical
25 with someone else walking down the street singing too.
I wait to see how the plot ends
because it's my story
and I choose the cast
and I'm directing.

Respond

How does seeing a rainbow affect you? Were you as uplifted by the experience as the speaker in this poem is?

Words to Know

remnants (REM nuntz) *n.*: Leftover parts (line 15)
etched (ECHT) *v.*: Drawn or engraved (line 20)

Lorna Dee Cervantes (1954–   )
Q: What did Cervantes like to read while growing up?
A: By the time she was twelve, Cervantes was reading aloud the English Romantic poets, such as Byron, Keats, and Shelley, to get a feel for the rhythms of the English language.
Q: When did Cervantes start writing poetry?
A: She wrote her first poem at the age of eight and put together her first collection of poetry at fifteen. She published some of these poems in her high school newspaper.

Activities

MAKE MEANING

Explore Your Reading

Look Back (Recall)

1. In "Voice," what kind of landscape does the speaker's voice become at school? At home?
2. In "This Morning . . .," where is the speaker and what time of day and year is it?

Think It Over (Interpret)

3. Which words describe the speaker's attitudes in "Voice"? How are the attitudes different?
4. What does the speaker in "This Morning . . ." mean when she says that she feels as if she's in a movie?

Go Beyond (Apply)

5. Which places in your life are "flatlands" to you? Which places make you feel as if you're walking in the midst of rainbows?

Develop Reading and Literary Skills

Understand Speakers in Poetry

Every poem has a distinct **speaker**, who expresses the poem's thoughts and feelings. Even two poems that deal with similar ideas will have two different speakers. In reading "Voice" and "This Morning . . .," you encounter speakers who are very different from each other. What are your impressions of each speaker's age, personality, likes, and dislikes?

Complete a chart like this one to help you identify the characteristics of these speakers.

	Speaker in "Voice"	Speaker in "This Morning . . ."
Location:		
Personality:		
Likes:	sierras	rainbows
Dislikes:		
Mood(s):		

1. Use the details in your chart to formulate an image of each speaker. Write a one-sentence summary that describes the speaker in each poem.
2. How does your image of the speaker help you understand the poem?

Ideas for Writing

The speakers in these poems use specific images to express their ideas and feelings.

Comparison-Contrast Essay Using the notes you made on your chart, write two paragraphs comparing and contrasting the speakers in "Voice" and "This Morning . . . ." For example, they are similar because they each respond to the mood of a specific place. Focus on the different attitudes expressed by the speakers in each poem.

Poem About You Create a speaker who sounds like an aspect of your personality, or of someone you know well. Write a poem using a specific image to describe that aspect. Develop the image with different details throughout the poem.

Ideas for Projects

Collage Assemble a collage made up of photographs and drawings of yourself with many different expressions on your face. Include captions explaining the different "voices" of your personality shown in each image.

Audio or Video Recording Write and record a monologue that expresses a specific attitude or mood. Play your recording for a group and ask them to help you evaluate how effectively it expresses the attitude or mood.

How Am I Doing?

Take a moment to respond to these questions in your journal:

How do I recognize the speaker of a poem?
Which piece of my work shows how I best express my voice?

How would you communicate if you weren't able to speak?

Reach Into Your Background

Imagine how it would feel to be unable to see, hear, or speak. How would you communicate? Helen Keller was left blind, deaf, and speechless from a childhood bout with scarlet fever. What other ways could she get information and express herself?

Try this experiment with a partner: Blindfold yourself and do not speak. Have your partner lead you from one side of the classroom to another and back. You must communicate this intention to your partner nonverbally—without words. Then tell the class how you communicated to your partner.

Read Actively
Identify a Character's Problems and Solutions

If you found that you couldn't speak, you would need to find other ways to communicate. In a group, list the things you might do (such as write or draw) to solve the problem so that you could express your needs and feelings.

Identifying **problems** faced by characters in literature along with the **solutions** they come up with will help you better understand the characters. You may even come up with ideas for solving some of your own problems!

As you read this autobiographical piece, use a chart like this to list the steps that Helen Keller takes to solve problems and accomplish her goal. Begin by stating Helen's goal. Then list the problems or obstacles she faced. Under each problem, state the action she took to overcome each problem.

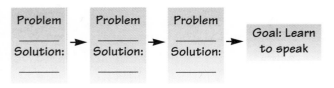

Problem	Problem	Problem	Goal: Learn to speak
Solution:	Solution:	Solution:	

I Learn to Speak

from **The Story of My Life**

Helen Keller

It was in the spring of 1890 that I learned to speak. The impulse to utter audible sounds had always been strong within me. I used to make noises, keeping one hand on my throat while the other hand felt the movements of my lips. I was pleased with anything that made a noise and liked to feel the cat purr and the dog bark. I also liked to keep my hand on a singer's throat, or on a piano when it was being played. Before I lost my sight and hearing, I was fast learning to talk, but after my illness it was found that I had ceased to speak because I could not hear. I used to sit in my mother's lap all day long and keep my hands on her face because it amused me to feel the motions of her lips; and I moved my lips, too, although I had forgotten what talking was. My friends say that I laughed and cried naturally, and for awhile I made many sounds and word-elements, not because they were a means of communication, but because the need for exercising my vocal organs was imperative. There was, however, one word the

> 📖 **Read Actively**
>
> **Visualize** what your world would be like if you couldn't see or hear.

Words to Know

audible (AW duh buhl) *adj.*: Able to be heard
ceased (SEEST) *v.*: Stopped
imperative (ihm PER uh tihv) *adj.*: Absolutely necessary

meaning of which I still remembered, *water.* I pronounced it "wa-wa." Even this became less and less intelligible until the time when Miss Sullivan began to teach me. I stopped using it only after I had learned to spell the word on my fingers.

I had known for a long time that the people about me used a method of communication different from mine; and even before I knew that a deaf child could be taught to speak, I was conscious of dissatisfaction with the means of communication I already possessed. One who is entirely dependent upon the manual alphabet has always a sense of restraint, of narrowness. This feeling began to agitate me with a vexing, forward-reaching sense of a lack that should be filled. My thoughts would often rise and beat up like birds against the wind; and I persisted in using my lips and voice. Friends tried to discourage this tendency, fearing lest it would lead to disappointment. But I persisted, and an accident soon occurred which resulted in the breaking down of this great barrier—I heard the story of Ragnhild Kaata.

📖 **Read Actively**

Make an inference about Helen's character, based on her actions in trying to use words.

In 1890 Mrs. Lamson, who had been one of Laura Bridgman's teachers, and who had just returned from a visit to Norway and Sweden, came to see me, and told me of Ragnhild Kaata, a deaf and blind girl in Norway who had actually been taught to speak. Mrs. Lamson had scarcely finished telling me about this girl's success before I was on fire with eagerness. I resolved that I, too, would learn to speak. I would not rest satisfied until my teacher took me, for advice and assistance, to Miss Sarah Fuller, principal of the Horace Mann School. This lovely, sweet-natured lady offered to teach me herself, and we began the twenty-sixth of March, 1890.

Miss Fuller's method was this: she passed my hand lightly over her face, and let me feel the position of her tongue and lips when she made a sound. I was eager to imitate every motion and in an hour had learned six elements of speech: M, P, A, S, T, I. Miss Fuller gave me eleven lessons in all. I shall never forget the surprise and delight I felt when I uttered my first connected sentence, "It is warm." True, they were broken and stammering syllables; but they were human speech. My soul, conscious of new strength, came out of bondage, and was reaching through those broken symbols of speech to all knowledge and all faith.

Words to Know

vexing (VECK sing) *adj.*: Troubling
perseverance (per suh VEER uhns) *n.*: Steady determination
contend (kuhn TEND) *v.*: Struggle; fight
ecstatically (ek STAT ihk lee) *adv.*: Joyfully

No deaf child who has earnestly tried to speak the words which he has never heard—to come out of the prison of silence, where no tone of love, no song of bird, no strain of music ever pierces the stillness—can forget the thrill of surprise, the joy of discovery which came over him when he uttered his first word. Only such a one can appreciate the eagerness with which I talked to my toys, to stones, trees, birds, and dumb animals, or the delight I felt when at my call Mildred ran to me or my dogs obeyed my commands. It is an unspeakable boon to me to be able to speak in winged words that need no interpretation. As I talked, happy thoughts fluttered up out of my words that might perhaps have struggled in vain to escape my fingers.

But it must not be supposed that I could

📖 **Read Actively**

Identify a problem
Helen will need to resolve in order to learn to speak.

really talk in this short time. I had learned only the elements of speech. Miss Fuller and Miss Sullivan could understand me, but most people would not have understood one word in a hundred. Nor is it true that, after I had learned these elements, I did the rest of the work myself. But for Miss Sullivan's genius, untiring perseverance and devotion, I could not have progressed as far as I have toward natural speech. In the first place, I labored night and day before I could be understood even by my most intimate friends; in the second place, I needed Miss Sullivan's assistance constantly in my efforts to articulate each sound clearly and to combine all sounds

in a thousand ways. Even now she calls my attention every day to mispronounced words.

All teachers of the deaf know what this means, and only they can at all appreciate the peculiar difficulties with which I had to contend. In reading my teacher's lips I was wholly dependent on my fingers: I had to use the sense of touch in catching the vibrations of the throat, the movements of the mouth and the expression of the face; and often this sense was at fault. In such cases I was forced to repeat the words or sentences, sometimes for hours, until I felt the proper ring in my own voice. My work was practice, practice, practice. Discouragement and weariness cast me down frequently; but the next moment the thought that I should soon be at home and show my loved ones what I had accomplished, spurred me on, and I eagerly looked forward to their pleasure in my achievement.

"My little sister will understand me now," was a thought stronger than all obstacles. I used to repeat ecstatically, "I am not dumb now." I could not be despondent while I anticipated the delight of talking to my mother and reading her responses from her lips. It astonished me to find how much easier it is to talk than to spell with the fingers, and I discarded the manual alphabet as a medium of communication on my part; but Miss Sullivan and a few friends still use it in speaking to me, for it is more convenient and more rapid than lip-reading.

Just here, perhaps, I had better explain our use of the manual alphabet, which seems to puzzle people who do not know us. One who reads or talks to me spells with his hand, using the single-hand manual alphabet generally employed by the deaf. I place my hand on the hand of the speaker so lightly as not to impede its movements. The position of the hand is as easy to feel as it is to see. I do not feel each letter any more than you see each letter separately when you read. Constant practice makes the fingers very flexible, and some of my friends spell rapidly—about as fast as an expert writes on a typewriter. The mere spelling is, of course, no more a conscious act than it is in writing.

When I had made speech my own, I could not wait to go home. At last the happiest of happy moments arrived. I had made my homeward journey, talking constantly to Miss Sullivan, not for the sake of talking, but determined to improve to the last minute. Almost before I knew it, the train stopped at the Tuscumbia station, and there on the platform stood the whole family. My eyes fill with tears now as I think how my mother pressed me close to her, speechless and trembling with delight, taking in every syllable that I spoke, while little Mildred seized my free hand and kissed it and danced, and my father expressed his pride and affection in a big silence. It was as if Isaiah's prophecy[1] had been fulfilled in me, "The mountains and the hills shall break forth before you into singing, and all the trees of the field shall clap their hands!"

---

1. **Isaiah's prophecy** (ay SAY uhz PRAHF uh see) *n.*: A prediction in the Old Testament book of Isaiah.

Words to Know

impede (ihm PEED) *v.*: Make difficult

Respond

- How would you feel if you had broken through silence and learned to speak?
- Would you have learned to speak if you had had to overcome the obstacles that Helen Keller faced? Why or why not?

Helen Keller

(1880–1968)

Childhood: As the result of a severe fever, Helen Keller became permanently blind and deaf at the age of nineteen months. She later wrote, "I knew my own mind well enough and always had my own way, even if I had to fight tooth and nail for it."

Meeting someone famous: When Helen was a small child, her father took her to Washington, D.C., to be examined by Dr. Alexander Graham Bell, who gave advice about the girl's education.

Constant companion: Anne Sullivan, a teacher nearly blind herself, arrived in the Keller household when Helen was six and spent hours each day teaching her to use the manual alphabet.

First book: Keller wrote *The Story of My Life* during her years at Radcliffe College, from which she graduated with honors.

Honors: Keller received the Presidential Medal of Freedom from Lyndon Johnson in 1964.

Activities

MAKE MEANING

Explore Your Reading

Look Back (Recall)

1. Before she learned to speak, how did Helen Keller communicate?

Think It Over (Interpret)

2. Why was it so important to Helen to be able to speak?
3. What does Helen mean when she says, "My thoughts would often rise and beat up like birds against the wind"?
4. What does Helen's account of her struggle to speak show about her character?

Go Beyond (Apply)

5. Some people feel that "signing"—using the hand alphabet—should not be viewed as inferior to speech. What would Helen Keller say to them?

Develop Reading and Literary Skills

Understand Character

In telling the story of her life, Helen Keller describes how she solved almost overwhelming problems. Her experience is inspirational because she shares each painful step she took to advance her ability to communicate. As you follow her progress, you observe the strengths in her character that enable her to succeed.

1. Using the information from your problem-solution chart, summarize the problems Helen had to overcome in learning to speak.
2. What do the solutions that Helen came up with reveal about her character?

Ideas for Writing

Helen Keller has inspired thousands of people, even those whose sight, speech, and hearing are not impaired.

Firsthand Biography Choose a person who has inspired you, perhaps in solving a problem. Write about the important things that you learned from that person. Use specific details and events to tell about what happened.

Another Point of View Retell the story of Helen's learning to speak from the point of view of Anne Sullivan. Describe the problems your student faced and her responses to the challenges. Include how Helen's accomplishments were an inspiration to you.

Ideas for Projects

Research Report Helen made use of every system of communication available to her. Work with a partner to research and learn signing, lip reading, or Braille (the alphabet for the blind). Present the results of your learning and teaching in an oral report to the class. [Science Link]

Communication Bulletin Board Some developments in communication offer sight- or hearing-impaired people options not available to Helen Keller. With a group, investigate a system of communication, such as the telegraph, telephone, radio, television, or computer network. Research when the system was invented, what it can and cannot do, the technology that is involved, how it works, and how widely it is used today. Share your information with the class. [Science Link]

How Am I Doing?

Evaluate your understanding by writing responses in your journal to these questions:

How well can I communicate without using words?

What have I learned about how characters solve problems?

The Kid Nobody Could Handle by Kurt Vonnegut, Jr.
dramatized by Christopher Sergel

How do you relate to someone whose style is completely different from yours?

Reach Into Your Background

Think about how you might react to someone who is very different from you—who dresses differently, talks differently, and seems to have completely different interests from yours. Thinking about this situation, do one of these activities:

- In your journal, describe an experience in which you meet someone whose style is completely different from yours. How do you respond at first and later on?
- Imagine that you and this other person have to come to an agreement about some issue on which you disagree. With a partner, role-play the two sides of the discussion. Analyze what needs to be done in order to arrive at a solution both sides can live with.

Read Actively
Predict Characters' Behavior

Remember a situation when you expected someone you knew to behave in a certain way. You probably based your expectation on that person's past behavior, your own past experiences, and maybe a wild hunch or two.

When you read a work of literature, you react to the characters almost as if they were real people. You watch their behavior and try to figure them out. You develop expectations about them—what they are feeling, why they act in a certain way. Based on your observations, you can begin to **predict** how they will behave in certain situations.

Refer to the list of characters at the beginning of the play. Predict how each will react in a situation that revolves around a "problem" student. As you read, continue to jot down predictions about how you expect the characters to behave.

City Street, 1955 David Park
Sheldon Memorial Art Gallery, University of Nebraska

The Kid Nobody Could Handle

Kurt Vonnegut, Jr.
dramatized by Christopher Sergel

Characters
Newt, observer
Margie, waitress
George Helmholtz, high school music
　teacher
Grace Helmholtz, his wife
Bert Quinn, restaurant owner
Jim Donnini, a problem young man
Mrs. Crane, English teacher

[*The curtain is rising to reveal a
stage with several playing areas.*

*At right, there's a suggestion of
a portion of a quite ordinary small
restaurant. All that's required is a
small table with a checked cloth and
two chairs. If desired, however, this
can be elaborated with another table
or so and perhaps a section of*

counter. There should be a parking meter standing in front and to the side of the restaurant area.

At upstage center and to stage left, there are several chairs arranged as classroom seats, teacher's desk and a locker. A small podium at left, facing front, and any other available props that would suggest a high school music room. A few instrument cases placed beside the locker would be helpful.

A small, humorless man, BERT QUINN, *is revealed sitting at the restaurant table toying sourly with some food on the plate before him. If desired, a few extras may be seen crossing downstage, either to right or left, apparently on the sidewalk.]*

NEWT. *[As curtain is rising]* It's early morning—some people going to work, some to school. *[Indicates right]* That's Bert Quinn's restaurant. Bert eats his own food—not because he likes it, but because he saves money that way.

*[*MARGIE *is entering with a Silex full of coffee.]*

BERT. *[Calling right without looking up]* Margie——

MARGIE. *[As she's pouring more coffee into his cup]* Yes, Mr. Quinn?

BERT. I'd like more— *[Realizing]* Thank you. Did the Kid finish mopping?

MARGIE. No, sir.

BERT. *[Irritated]* Tell him—hurry, and then get to school.

MARGIE. *[As she's going; casually]* I tell him every morning.

NEWT. Bert isn't really a well man. He can't sleep, can't digest his food and can't stop working. He has only two moods: one suspicious, the other arrogant. The first applies when he's losing money, the second when he's making it. *[*NEWT *steps upstage a few steps and nods left.]* Over here is Lincoln High School—that large classroom is for the band—run by George

Helmholtz—whose head is always filled with band music.

*[*GEORGE HELMHOLTZ, *holding a car steering wheel as though driving, comes shuffling on left. His wife,* GRACE, *as though in the seat beside him, shuffles with him.]*

George is driving his wife to the bus before school this morning because she is going to spend a few days with relatives.

*[*GEORGE *apparently turns the car toward the audience and then apparently stops.]*

GEORGE. *[To his wife]* Before you go, I'd like a kiss.

GRACE. *[Looking about, embarrassed]* I kissed you before we left the house.

GEORGE. I'd like another.

[With a sigh, she gives him a brief kiss.]

NEWT. *[Summing up]* Very affectionate fellow.

GRACE. Try to collect from the school for the money you paid to get the music copied.

GEORGE. The minute I get there.

GRACE. *[Concerned]* I could've fixed breakfast for you.

GEORGE. I'll stop at Bert's restaurant.

GRACE. After he took such advantage of you on that land deal?

GEORGE. What's the difference? *[Affectionately]* How about another—

GRACE. *[Amused, apparently hopping out of car, carrying overnight bag]* Back in a few days.

GEORGE. *[Calling after her]* Phone me tonight.

*[*GRACE *goes off left while* GEORGE *apparently continues slowly right in car.]*

NEWT. *[Meanwhile]* Each year George dreams the same big dream. He dreams of leading as fine a band as there is on the face of the earth. And, in a sense, each year his dream comes true. It comes true because George is sure that a man couldn't have a better dream. Faced by his unnerving sureness, Kiwanians, Rotarians, and Lions[1] pay for band uniforms that cost twice as much as their best suits, school administrators let George raid the budget, and youngsters play their hearts out for him.

[During this, GEORGE *has apparently parked*

---

1. **Kiwanians** (kih WAH nee inz), **Rotarians** (roh TAHR ee inz), **and Lions:** Members of Kiwanis, Rotary, and Lions clubs, community-service organizations that help to support school and community activities.

the car near the restaurant—don't let the actor be elaborate—by propping the wheel against a standing parking meter.]

And when the youngsters don't have any talent, George gets them to play on guts alone.

[*Before going into restaurant,* GEORGE *glances about, sees he's alone, takes a step forward, and then raises his arms*

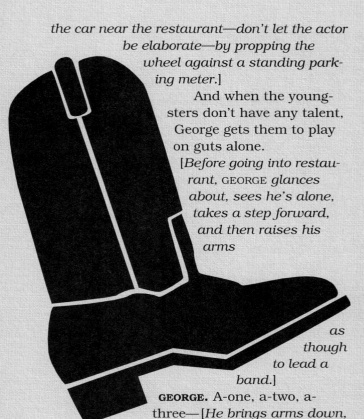

as though to lead a band.]

GEORGE. A-one, a-two, a-three—[*He brings arms down, and there's a burst of beautiful band music that he apparently leads for several seconds. He gestures for the end, the sound cuts out—and humming the continuation of whatever music was played, he walks into restaurant.*]

[*NOTE: A rousing Sousa[2] march would be a good choice, and the sound cues should be carefully rehearsed.*]

NEWT. [*Smiling*] That music was all in George's head. But he cares so much he makes everyone hear it.

[GEORGE *is seating himself at the table with* BERT, *and the sounds of heavy construction work may begin here, though kept as background.*]

BERT. [*Calling right*] Fried eggs, coffee, and toast for Mr. Helmholtz.

NEWT. [*Wryly, toward sounds*] The noise of

---

2. **John Philip Sousa** (SOO suh): Famous American bandmaster (1854–1932) who composed many marches, including "Stars and Stripes Forever."

real life. Waddling, clanking, muddy machines tearing the hill behind the restaurant to pieces, with trucks hauling the pieces away. Those sounds put Bert in his arrogant and boastful mood.

BERT. How many eyes saw that hill back there before I did? Thousands, I'll bet. And not one saw what I saw. [*In wonder, chewing on toothpick*] How many eyes?

GEORGE. Mine, at least.

BERT. [*Amused*] Yours.

[MARGIE, *the waitress, is bringing tray to* GEORGE.]

GEORGE. [*Pleasantly*] All the hill meant to me was a hard climb, some free blackberries, taxes, and a place for band picnics. [*To* MARGIE] Thank you.

[*She exits.*]

BERT. You inherit the hill, and it's nothing but a pain in the neck. So you figure you'll stick me with it.

GEORGE. The price was more than fair.

BERT. [*Gleefully*] You say that now—now you see the shopping district's got to grow. Now you see what I saw.

[*A wiry young man, sullen, withdrawn, wearing jeans and gaudy shiny black boots with a jingling chain on them, is coming on, mopping mechanically.*]

GEORGE. [*As he's eating; not really interested*] Yes, but too late. Too late.

BERT. What do I do when I get your hill? [*Gestures toward sound*] I'm tearing down your hill. And now everybody wants to build a store where the hill was.

GEORGE. Um. [*Nodding to boy*] Hello [*Without response, the boy keeps mopping.*]

BERT. We all got something. You got music. I got vision.

Words to Know

unnerving (un NERV ihng) *adj.:* Upsetting

NEWT. [*Smiling*] And it's perfectly clear to Bert which one has the money.

BERT. Think big. That's what vision is. Keep your eyes wider than anybody else's.

GEORGE. [*Still regarding the mopper*] That boy. I've seen him around school, but I never knew his name.

BERT. [*Smiling cheerfully*] Billy the Kid. The storm trooper. Flash Gordon. [*Calling*] Hey, Jim! Come here a minute.

Read Actively

Predict how George will relate to Jim.

NEWT. [*As the sullen boy is approaching them, the mop dragging after*] George is pretty sensitive. What appalled him was to see that the boy's eyes were as expressionless as oysters.

BERT. This is my brother-in-law's kid by another marriage—before he married my sister. His name's Jim Donnini, and he's from the south side of Chicago and he's very tough.

GEORGE. How do you do?

JIM. [*Looking past him; emptily*] Hi.

BERT. He's living with me now. He's my baby now.

GEORGE. You want a lift to school, Jim?

BERT. [*As* JIM *doesn't reply*] He won't talk to me, either. But, yeah, he wants a lift to school. [*To* JIM. *Shortly*] Go on, kid, wash up and shave.

[*Robotlike,* JIM *goes off right, trailing the mop.*]

GEORGE. [*Concerned*] Where are his parents?

BERT. His mother's dead. His old man married my sister, walked out on her, and stuck her with him. Then the court didn't like the way she was raising him and put him in foster homes for a while. Then they decided to get him clear of Chicago, so they stuck me with him. [*Shaking his head*] Life's a funny thing, Helmholtz.

GEORGE. [*Pushing his eggs away*] Not very funny, sometimes.

BERT. [*Chewing toothpick*] Like some whole new race of people coming up. He's nothing like the decent kids we got around here. Did you notice those boots he wears? And he won't talk, won't run around with other kids, won't study. I don't think he can even read or write very good.

GEORGE. Does he like music at all? Or drawing? Does he collect anything?

BERT. You know what he likes—he likes to polish those boots. The only enjoyment he gets is when he's alone, comic books spread around, and polishing those boots. [*Remembering*] Oh, he had a collection, too. I took it away from him and threw it in the river.

GEORGE. Threw it in the river?

BERT. Yeah. Eight knives—some with blades as long as your hand.

GEORGE. Oh. [*Concerned*] This is a new problem at some schools, I guess. [*Wanting to sort it out*] It's kind of a sickness, isn't it? That's the way to look at it, wouldn't you say?

BERT. Yes, sick. [*Tapping his chest*] And Doctor Bert is just the man to give him what's good for his ailment.

GEORGE. What's that?

BERT. [*Hard*] For a start—no more talk about poor, little sick boy. That's all he's heard from social workers and the juvenile court.

[JIM, *still expressionless, is reentering right, now wearing a leather jacket.*]

GEORGE. But actually—

BERT. Actually he's a bum. Well, I'm going to ride his tail until he straightens up and flies right or winds up in the can[3] for life.

GEORGE. [*Nodding toward* Jim; *warning*] Bert—

BERT. [*Going right on*] One way or the other. [*Directly to* JIM] Believe it, boy!

GEORGE. I see. [*To* JIM] I'm parked in front. [*Without a response,* JIM *goes out to stand by the parking meter.* GEORGE *gets up, putting some money on the table.*] That right?

---

3. can: Slang for jail.

[BERT *nods, and* GEORGE *puts a separate coin by coffee cup. He's depressed.*]
If I knew anything to say to that boy.
BERT. [*Picking up money*] What's to say? Listen to those bulldozers—really tearing into it.
GEORGE. [*Preoccupied*] They are—they really are.
[*As he's going to join* JIM, BERT *reaches across, picks up the other coin, considers an instant, then goes out right.*]
BERT. [*Holding coin for her*] Margie—
[*Without talk,* GEORGE *takes up wheel, and he and* JIM *are apparently driving left. The construction sounds, if used, fade.*]
NEWT. George tried baseball, football, anything to get a conversation going, but nothing happened. And, of course, he couldn't help trying the most important subject in the world to him.
GEORGE. [*Glancing at* JIM

📖 **Read Actively**

Connect your experiences with George's. Have you ever tried to reach out to someone who didn't respond?

and clearing his throat] Do you—do you like listening to music?
[JIM *sighs heavily with boredom.*]
[GEORGE *tries again.*] Ever drum with your fingers or keep time with your feet?
[JIM *leans his head back, closing his eyes, waiting for* GEORGE *to give up.* GEORGE *tries another approach.*] Those boots—what's the function of the chains? Are they to jingle?
[JIM *looks away, but* GEORGE *presses on.*] At least you whistle. Even whistling—it can be like picking up the keys to a whole new world.

Boy and Car, 1955 David Park, Salander O'Reilly Galleries

JIM. [*Contemptuously*] A new world—
GEORGE. [*Eagerly*] A world as beautiful as any world can be. [JIM *makes a soft Bronx cheer, but* GEORGE *continues undaunted.*]

There! You've illustrated the basic principle of the family of brass wind instruments. The glorious voice of every one of them starts with a buzz on the lips.
[*Apparently they've reached a parking place at left, and they're both facing forward.*]
JIM. [*Fishing out a cigarette from inside of his leather jacket*] Any time.

Words to Know

contemptuously (kuhn TEMP choo uhs lee) *adv*.: Scornfully
undaunted (uhn DAWN ted) *adj*.: Not frightened

GEORGE. [*Noticing as* JIM *lights cigarette, keeping casual*] That—that won't do your lungs much good.

[JIM's *reply is to expel some smoke.* GEORGE *speaks carefully.*]

Sometimes I get disgusted, too, and I don't see how I can stand it. I feel like doing all kinds of crazy things—things that might even be bad for me.

[JIM *expels more smoke.*]

And then—[*Snaps fingers on left hand and grabs wheel again enthusiastically*] And then, Jim, I remember I've got at least one tiny corner of the universe I can make just the way I want it. I can go to it, and enjoy it till I'm brand-new and happy again.

JIM. Aren't you the lucky one?

GEORGE. I am, for a fact. My corner of the universe happens to be the air around my head. I can fill it with music.

[JIM *is yawning, apparently getting out of the car.* GEORGE *continues eagerly.*]

Mr. Beeler, in zoology, has his butterflies. Mr. Trottman, in physics, has his pendulum. Mrs. Crane, in English, her books—

JIM. [*Contemptuously*] Mrs. Crane—

GEORGE. Making sure everybody has a corner like that is about the biggest job we teachers have. I—

[*But he's stopped as* JIM *drops cigarette and walks out left.*]

Jim— [*But the boy is gone. Unhappily,* GEORGE *places wheel by post or sets it off left, then steps on the remainder of* JIM's *cigarette, scoops it into his hand, and takes it with him into his classroom, where he puts it in a wastebasket.*]

NEWT. [*Meanwhile*] George Helmholtz's first class of the morning was C Band. C Band is where beginners thumped and wheezed and tooted as best they could, and looked down the long, long road through B Band to A Band, the Lincoln High School Ten Square Band, the finest school band in the world.

[GEORGE *is coming up onto the podium left, holding a baton.*]

Words to Know

podium (POH dee uhm) *n.*: A low platform for a conductor

GEORGE. [*Speaking front, addressing imaginary class*] Good morning, C Band. I know it's early—none of us warmed up yet. [*Raising his baton*] But remember this— [*Believing it*] You're better than you think you are! A-one, a-two, a-three . . . [*Down comes the baton, and with it there's the sound of magnificent band music.*]

NEWT. [*As* GEORGE *continues to lead*] Sounds great for C Band, doesn't it? [*Shaking his head*] That music you're hearing isn't C Band. What that is—it's what George was hearing—in his head—the music as it was going to be—some day! Actually C Band set out in its quest for beauty—set out like a rusty switch engine, with valves stuck, pipes clogged, unions leaking, bearings dry— [GEORGE *is singing yump-yumps along with band as he brings this passage to a close.*]

NEWT. And George was still smiling at the end of that class hour.

GEORGE. [*Front*] Thanks. Thank you very much. See you tomorrow. [*With this, he's getting off the podium and coming forward into what is the beginning of some student* (EXTRAS) *traffic crossing downstage to left or to right, talking excitedly to each other as they cross. Note:* MARGIE *and* GRACE, *with minor costume changes to look like students, may do this.*]

STUDENTS. [*Generally*] No, it's true! . . . How do you know? . . . Mr. Beller was telling Mr. Trottman . . . I heard Mrs. Crane was crying . . . You're outa your mind . . . Can't be true . . . So how come her classes are canceled? Tomorrow, too.

NEWT. [*During above*] George had gone into the hall for a drink of water, but he couldn't figure out what the students were talking about.

[*The students are going off, leaving a confused* GEORGE *behind. As he looks left,* JIM *walks in, pausing to polish his boots on his pants leg.*]

GEORGE. Hello, Jim. What's going on? [JIM *shrugs.*] I have to get back for rehearsal with B Band—but I was thinking about you. The school has a lot of clubs and teams that meet after classes. It's a good way to get to know a lot of the other students.

JIM. [*Coldly*] Maybe I don't want to know a lot of the other students. [*Walking past* GEORGE; *heading right*] Ever think of that? [*As he's going off right*, JIM *walks hard to make the boot chains jingle.*]

[MRS. CRANE, *a worried English teacher, is coming on left.*]

MRS. CRANE. [*Keeping herself calm with an effort*] George—

GEORGE. Mrs. Crane—I just heard your name—some of the students—

MRS. CRANE. [*Unhappily*] Can't hush it up. I suppose it's all over the school. Will you be at the faculty meeting?

GEORGE. Meeting?

MRS. CRANE. A special meeting this afternoon—on vandalism.

GEORGE. [*With casual concern*] I hear that some schools—

MRS. CRANE. [*Cutting in*] My office was wrecked last night.

GEORGE. [*Stunned*] Your office? Here?

MRS. CRANE. [*Swallowing with difficulty*] I keep searching my mind—whom I might've offended—where I might've done less than I should for some student.

GEORGE. [*Incredulous*] You said—wrecked?

MRS. CRANE. Books, diplomas, records, all the snapshots of my trip to England—ripped, crumpled, trampled, drenched with ink!

GEORGE. [*Aghast*] No—

MRS. CRANE. [*With an unhappy laugh*] Also the beginnings of eleven novels. I don't suppose they were very good, but I'd rather destroy them myself.

GEORGE. [*Can hardly talk*] I can't believe it!

MRS. CRANE. The meeting—for whatever it's worth—is at four. [*Starting right. Speaking mainly to herself*] Is it my fault? Is it their fault? What's happening?

[*As she is going off right, and as the shocked* GEORGE *is going off left, the lights are dimming except for a spot on* NEWT *at downstage right.*]

NEWT. [*During this*] George was sickened. He couldn't believe it. And with his wife away, he had no one to discuss it with. It didn't become real to George until late that night, in a dream. In the dream, George saw a boy with barracuda[4] teeth, with claws like baling hooks.[5] The monster climbed into the band rehearsal room and started clawing to tatters the heads of the biggest and best drums in the state. George woke up terrified. There was nothing to do but to dress and go to school. [*The stage is still dark, but* GEORGE *has come into the classroom area at left with a lighted flashlight.*]

📖 **Read Actively**

Ask yourself why George is so upset that he has a nightmare.

George let himself in with his key and used a

---

4. **barracuda** (ba ruh KOO duh): A very fierce fish.
5. **baling** (BAY ling) **hooks:** Large hooks used for lifting heavy bundles.

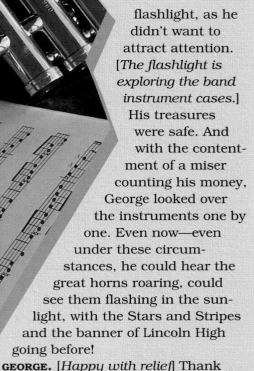

flashlight, as he didn't want to attract attention. [*The flashlight is exploring the band instrument cases.*] His treasures were safe. And with the contentment of a miser counting his money, George looked over the instruments one by one. Even now—even under these circumstances, he could hear the great horns roaring, could see them flashing in the sunlight, with the Stars and Stripes and the banner of Lincoln High going before!

GEORGE. [*Happy with relief*] Thank Heaven!

NEWT. Then George heard a noise in the chemistry lab next door.

[*The flashlight snaps out.*]

George went out into the hall, then jerked open the lab door.

[*The flashlight comes on again, revealing* JIM *holding a bottle that he has tilted over to pour.*]

GEORGE. You! You!

NEWT. Jim Donnini was splashing acid over the periodic table of the elements, over the books, over the bust of Lavoisier.[6] It was the most repulsive thing George had ever seen.

GEORGE. [*Horrified*] Put that down and get out of there!

JIM. What're you gonna do?

GEORGE. [*In shock*] I don't know. Clean up. Save what I can. But come out of there—come to my classroom. [*They're moving left.*]

JIM. You gonna call the fuzz?

GEORGE. [*Bewildered*] Call the fuzz?

> 📖 **Read Actively**
>
> **Connect** with Jim's feelings. Why do you think he is so angry?

JIM. [GEORGE *is so stupid.*] The cops!

[GEORGE *apparently turns on the lights in his classroom area.*]

GEORGE. I—I don't know. Put down the bottle of acid.

[JIM *does.* GEORGE *is confused and miserable. No thoughts come.*] If I'd caught you hurting the band instruments, probably I'd have hit you. [*Bothered by himself*] But I wouldn't have had any intelligent thoughts about what you were—what you thought you were doing.

JIM. [*Bravado*] It's about time this place got set on its ear.

GEORGE. Is it? [*Struggling with concern*] That must be so, if one of our students wants to murder it.

JIM. What good is it?

GEORGE. Not much, I guess. [*Unhappily*] But it's the best thing human beings have managed to do yet.

JIM. [*With contempt*]. The best thing—

GEORGE. [*Swallowing*]. Jim, if you smashed up all the school, we wouldn't have any hope.

JIM. What hope?

[GEORGE *considers a moment.*]

GEORGE. The hope that someday everybody will be glad they're alive. [*Takes a breath*] Even you.

JIM. That's a laugh. All I ever got out of this garbage pile was a hard time. [*Calculating*] So what're you gonna do?

Words to Know

incredulous (in KREJ oo luhs) *adj.:* Not believing
aghast (uh GAST) *adj.:* Horrified
bravado (bruh VAH doh) *n.:* A show of pretended courage

---

6. Lavoisier (lah VWAH zee ay): Antoine Laurent Lavoisier (1743–1794), a French chemist who pioneered in the study of oxygen.

GEORGE. [*Realizing*] I have to do something, don't I?

JIM. [*Contemptuously polishing a boot on his pants leg*] I don't care what you do!

GEORGE. Isn't there anything you care about? Anything, but those boots?

JIM. [*Challenging*] Go on. Call up whoever you're gonna call—Go ahead!

GEORGE. [*An agony of indecision; speaking mainly to himself*] I don't want to turn you in! I want to find some way to reach— [*Breaks off as he's struck by new thought. Rushing to get something from the locker nearby. As he takes something from locker*] I'll show you—you'll see—maybe this will convince— [*He brings velvet-covered object toward JIM.*] There! [*He takes velvet away, revealing a brightly polished trumpet.*] There's my treasure! It's the dearest thing I own. [*He thrusts it into JIM's hands.*] I give it to you. Do what you please with it. If you want, you can smash it—and I won't move a muscle to stop you. It's yours!

[*JIM is holding the trumpet uncertainly.*]

Go on! If the world has treated you so badly, it deserves to have that trumpet smashed.

JIM. [*Tossing trumpet on desk; polishing boot again*] I—I don't want it.

GEORGE. Jim— [*Exploding*] Those—boots! [*GEORGE grabs JIM's belt, puts a foot behind him, and dumps him onto the floor.*]

JIM. Hey! What are you—

[*GEORGE is jerking JIM's gaudy boots off—they should fit loosely to come off easily—and throwing them in corner.*]

GEORGE. [*As he's doing it; savagely*] I'll

📖 **Read Actively**

Predict what Jim will do with the trumpet.

show you! There! [*He pulls JIM to his feet again.*] All right—I've taken them!

[*JIM has apparently lost his socks with the boots. He stands looking down at his bare feet, shivering as though intensely cold. GEORGE shoves the trumpet back into JIM's hands.*]

Listen to me. You have to know what you have in your hand. That trumpet?

[*JIM just stands, holding it.*]

The special thing about it—it belonged to John Philip Sousa! And I'm trading it to you—for your boots. It's yours, Jim. John Philip Sousa's trumpet! It's worth hundreds of dollars, maybe thousands—

JIM. [*In a tight voice*] I don't want—

GEORGE. It's better than boots. You can learn to play it. You're somebody, Jim. You're the boy with John Philip Sousa's trumpet. [*They stand facing each other for a moment. The energy goes out of GEORGE. He expels a breath.*]

GEORGE. [*Subdued*] I'll drive you home. I won't say a word about tonight. [*Crossing to apparent light switch*] I better turn these lights out.

JIM. Can I have my boots?

GEORGE. No. I don't think they're good for you. [*Apparently he turns off the lights, and for a moment the stage is dark. Then the industrial sound of bulldozers, if used, comes on again and so do the stage lights, generally revealing GEORGE and BERT eating breakfast again, and NEWT standing at downstage right.*]

NEWT. The next morning the waddling, clanking muddy machines were making the vision of Bert Quinn true. They were smoothing off the place where the hill had been behind the restaurant.

BERT. Eating out two mornings in a row? Something wrong at home?

GEORGE. My wife's still visiting relatives.

BERT. [*Winking*] While the cat's away—

GEORGE. When the cat's away, this mouse gets hungry.

[*JIM is coming on mopping as before, except now he wears some old gym shoes. The industrial noise, once registered, fades.*]

BERT. [*Leaning forward*] Is that what got you out of bed in the middle of the night? [*Jerks* head toward JIM] Kid! Go get Mr. Helmholtz his horn.

[JIM *raises his head and looks directly at* GEORGE *for an instant, then goes off right again, trailing the mop after him.*]

NEWT. [*During this*] What upset George—the boy's eyes were again as expressionless as oysters.

BERT. [*Irritated*] You take away his boots and give him a horn, and I'm not supposed to get curious? I'm not supposed to start asking questions?

GEORGE. I was going to—

BERT. [*Going right on; his voice rising*] I'm not supposed to find out you caught him taking the school apart? And it wasn't the first time.

GEORGE. I know, but —

BERT. [*Interrupting again*] You'd make a lousy crook. You'd leave your baton, sheet music, and your driver's license at the scene of the crime.

GEORGE. I don't think about hiding clues.

BERT. [*Derisively*] You don't think about anything.

GEORGE. I just do what I do. The reason I came for breakfast, I wanted to discuss with you about—

BERT. [*Sharply*] Nothing to discuss.

GEORGE. [*Uneasily*] What do you mean?

BERT. All over with Jim and me. Last night was the payoff.

GEORGE. What will you do?

BERT. I'm sending him back where he came from.

GEORGE. To another string of foster homes?

BERT. Whatever the experts figure out to do with such a kid.

[*He sits back, relieved that he's said it.* GEORGE *takes this in, and he's very concerned.*]

GEORGE. [*A decision*] You can't.

BERT. [*Almost laughter*] I can.

GEORGE. But that will be the end of him.

BERT. Why?

GEORGE. [*Strong*] Because he can't stand to be thrown away like that one more time.

BERT. [*Getting up angrily*] Him? He can't feel anything. I can't help him—I can't hurt him.

[JIM *is coming on right, impassively holding the trumpet.*]

BERT. There isn't a nerve or feeling in him.

GEORGE. A bundle of scar tissue.

BERT. [*Aware of him*] Kid—give back the horn.

[JIM *puts the trumpet on the table.*]

GEORGE. No, Jim. [*Forcing a smile*] It's yours.

BERT. He doesn't want it. Take it while you got the chance.

GEORGE. [*Continuing, to* JIM] I gave it to you.

BERT. All he'll do is swap it for a knife or a pack of cigarettes.

GEORGE. [*Without turning to* BERT] He doesn't know what it is yet. It takes awhile to find out.

BERT. Is it any good?

GEORGE. Any good? [*Incredulous*] It belonged to John Philip Sousa.

BERT. Who?

GEORGE. [*Getting up uncertainly, his voice hushed with emotion*] Who was John Philip Sousa? [GEORGE *picks up the trumpet, utterly inarticulate.*]

Read Actively

Ask yourself what George means by "scar tissue."

Words to Know

derisively (di RĪ siv lee) *adv*.: In a ridiculing way

The Kid Nobody Could Handle K·37

NEWT. The subject was too big and George was too exhausted to cover it. [*As* BERT *and* JIM *watch, each in his way bewildered,* GEORGE *kisses the cold mouthpiece and fingers the valves professionally.*]

NEWT. [*During this*] There was nothing George could say or show them. They were deaf to him, and blind. And all George could see was the futility of men and their treasures. He'd thought this greatest treasure he owned could buy a soul for a troubled boy. But his trumpet was worthless. [*With a cry,* GEORGE *suddenly bangs the trumpet on the edge of the table, then again. NOTE: This can be done with a substitute piece of metal so it can't be seen by audience.*]

BERT. Hey! What are ya— [GEORGE *is banging trumpet on floor behind table and then apparently stamps on it.*]

BERT. You crazy! Nuts!

Read Actively

Predict how Jim will respond to George's banging the trumpet.

[GEORGE, *totally exhausted, tosses trumpet back onto table.*]

BERT. Ya busted it! Why'd ya do that?

[GEORGE *is shaking his head.*] What's that prove?

GEORGE. I—I don't know. I—excuse me—I want to go.

BERT. You're leaving the busted—

GEORGE. [*Sharply*] Yes!

BERT. Why?

GEORGE. [*Welling out of him*] Because life's no good. [GEORGE, *utterly miserable, is going off left uncertainly as the others watch.*]

NEWT. [*Quietly*] There was one thing GEORGE didn't notice. He didn't notice the eyes of Jim Donnini. Suddenly those eyes filled with pity and with alarm. They became human. They came alive.

[JIM *picks up the trumpet and goes out right.* BERT *looks after him thoughtfully and then follows him off.*]

[*As this happens*] The surprising thing—somehow Bert Quinn caught the change—and something like hope flickered for the first time in Bert's bitterly lonely face. [NEWT *is alone now on the stage.*] There were some unanswered questions when the new semester began two weeks later at Lincoln High. [*Smiles as he goes off right*] But life was about to deal with them.

[*With his exit, students are crossing downstage to right and left, moving energetically and talking to each other as they go. This can include* GRACE, MARGIE, *and* MRS. CRANE, *all dressed as students.*]

STUDENTS. [*Generally*] Is there practice for C Band or not? . . . How do I know? . . . There was supposed to be an announcement if it was canceled . . . Well, check the bulletin board . . . How can I check when C Band is the first practice? . . . What's wrong with Mr. Helmholtz? . . . Beats me. You'd think he had a death in his family!

[*During this last exchange,* GEORGE *is coming on left, holding his baton. The students, afraid he's overheard—which he has—hurry on off left.* GEORGE *turns to face the podium, his back to the audience, considering what to do.*]

[JIM, *holding the apparently repaired trumpet, enters right, crossing unseen toward* GEORGE.]

JIM. [*Speaking quietly*] Mr. Helmholtz—Mr. Helmholtz—

[GEORGE *turns slowly to see him.*] Is this where I come for C Band practice?

GEORGE. Yes. Yes, this is the place.

JIM. [*Indicating horn*] It was just bent a little. No trouble getting it fixed.

[*Happiness is coming back into* GEORGE, *but he speaks carefully.*]

GEORGE. I see.

JIM. [*Looking off left front*] Where should I sit?

GEORGE. [*Beginning to smile*] For a start—the

Words to Know

futility (fyoo TIL uh tee) *n.:* Sense of hopelessness

last seat of the worst trumpet section of the worst band in school.

JIM. [*Agreeably*] Right—

GEORGE. [*Cheerfully*] But with that trumpet— [*Suddenly filling with his old enthusiasm, he hurries up onto the podium.*]

GEORGE. Let's get started, C Band. What are we waiting for? Maybe you're C Band now, but—[*In a moment, he's stopped by his own happiness and enthusiasm flooding back.* JIM *still stands left, watching.*]

[*Speaking front; starting over*] Think of it this way. Our aim is to make the world sound more beautiful than it did when we came into it. [*With conviction*] It can be done. You can do it.

JIM. [*Bursting out of him*] How!

GEORGE. [*Pointing off left front*] You should be sitting in the trumpet section.

JIM. [*Backing off; as he goes*] But how? [JIM *has gone off left, now apparently a part of C Band.*]

GEORGE. [*After him*] Just—love yourself—and make your instrument sing about it. [*He raises his baton.*] A-one, a-two, a-three— [*Down comes the baton, and with this, rousing and triumphant band music—the magnificent band music* GEORGE *hears in his head— fills the theater.*]

[*The curtain falls.*]

Respond

- What would you have said to George if you had seen him damage his valuable trumpet?
- What advice would you give Jim about getting along in the school?

Many of the novels of **Kurt Vonnegut, Jr.,** (1922–   ) use devices of science-fiction writing, such as space travel and fantastic inventions, to tell bizarre, comic stories about wildly individual characters. *Cat's Cradle* reveals a worldwide conflict over possession of a destructive substance known as "ice-nine." The short story from which this play is dramatized is found in a collection aptly titled, *Welcome to the Monkey House.* Much of Vonnegut's outlook was influenced by his experience during World War II, when he was captured and imprisoned in a storage cellar below a slaughterhouse. There he survived the Dresden firebombing that killed more than a hundred thousand people and leveled the town. He wrote about the experience many years later by devising a time-traveling character named Billy Pilgrim to tell the story. *Slaughterhouse-Five* became a best-selling novel and was made into a movie.

Activities

MAKE MEANING

Explore Your Reading

Look Back (Recall)

1. What does Jim do to Mrs. Crane's desk and to the chemistry lab?
2. What does George do to his trumpet in front of Jim?

Think It Over (Interpret)

3. What does George's ability to hear great music from inexperienced musicians say about him?
4. Why does Jim behave as destructively as he does?
5. Why is George's treatment of Jim more successful than Bert's?

Go Beyond (Apply)

6. Should Jim have gone unpunished for his vandalism? Why or why not?

Develop Reading and Literary Skills

Analyze Conflict in Drama

As you read this play, you predicted how the characters might behave. Which characters acted as you expected they would? Which of their problems were predictable? Which characters surprised you? For example, did you expect George to damage his Sousa trumpet?

Like real people, characters in a play are involved in **conflicts**, struggles with opposing forces that they encounter. Conflicts can be external, such as with another character or a situation, or internal, within a character.

List four conflicts Jim encountered, from the beginning of the play to the last scene. Include at least one external conflict and one internal conflict. For each conflict, identify the response he made. Which of his responses were most successful?

Ideas for Writing

The success of a play depends largely on how effectively the characters resolve their central conflicts.

Play Review Write a review evaluating the play. Explain why you liked or didn't like it. Back up your opinion of the play by referring to specific events and characters and the resolution of the central conflicts. Did the play teach you anything?

Personal Letter Write a personal letter from Jim to Mrs. Crane, apologizing for and explaining why he wrecked her office. Use Jim's voice in the letter and include what he can do to make amends to her.

Ideas for Projects

Music Video Prepare a music video that uses characters from the play. Select an appropriate piece of music. Then choreograph the characters and videotape their performance. [Music Link]

Debate With another student, debate the following question: Should Jim be disciplined for his vandalism at the school? Each side should base its arguments on the events in the play.

How Am I Doing?

Take a moment to write your thoughts to the following in your journal:

What have I learned from this play about how characters respond to conflict?

Which piece of my work best shows the value of self-expression?

How Do I Express Myself?

Think Critically About the Selections

The selections you have read in this section explore the question "How do I express myself?" With a partner or a small group, complete one or more of the following activities to show your understanding of the question. You can present your responses orally or in writing.

1. Each of these selections presents a character who expresses himself or herself in an unusual way. Choose two characters from different selections. Compare and contrast their ways of expressing themselves. **(Compare and Contrast)**

2. Look at the art on this page. How do you think the character in the painting would answer the question "How do I express myself?" Use details of the art to support your answer. **(Make Inferences; Provide Evidence)**

3. Which character from these selections do you admire most? Why? How are you similar to this character? How are you different? What can you do to be more like this character? **(Compare and Contrast; Make Judgments)**

4. Which character's experience made you change your mind about something or see something about yourself in a new light? Explain how. **(Synthesize)**

Projects

 Poetic Music Video Express yourself by making a music video of a poem of your choice. Record your reading or reciting of a favorite

Student Art *G-Clef: The Music and Me*
Michael Schwikardt, Cranford High School
Cranford, New Jersey

poem and include music for background. Assemble illustrations, sets, or props to accompany your recording. If possible, videotape your presentation to help you evaluate it later. [Music Link]

Storyboard Timeline Create a visual expression of yourself by making a storyboard timeline of your life over several years, projecting one or two decades into the future. Decide on the major events of your life and illustrate each event on a storyboard. Be sure to show the events in the sequence in which they happened (or might happen) in your life. [Art Link]

Looking at The Short

Marie G. Lee

Terms to know

Character is the person or animal who takes part in the action.

Setting is the time and place of the action.

Plot is the sequence of events of a story.

Theme is the central message, concern, or insight into life expressed in a literary work.

Conflict is a struggle between opposing forces that causes the events of a plot.

Short stories are brief works of fiction that contain a central **conflict** and one or more **characters** who are involved in actions that make up the **plot.** Author Marie G. Lee shares insights about characters in her stories:

Often when I write, my characters end up surprising me. I know that the people in my story are supposed to be coming from my own mind, but often, I will start writing a character one way, and he or she will then promptly go off and do something completely different—sometimes in really exasperating ways.

Characters Have Their Way I have learned over the years that if a character *insists* on doing something, I have to just follow. For instance, in my novel *If It Hadn't Been for Yoon Jun*, I started writing about a seventh grader, Alice. Then I added an eighth grade girl, Dusty, so Alice could have an older friend. What I wasn't prepared for is that, later, Dusty would beat up a scary bully *and* get mad at Alice.

Of course, I want my characters to get along, just as if they were real people. However, like real people, characters have their differences and their communication problems, too. Sometimes the problems the characters have with each other—the conflicts—become a vital focus of the story itself. In other words, the story becomes a way to examine conflicts between people. When I let Dusty "do her thing," she got mad at Alice when Alice stood by while a bully threatened a new kid. However, what Dusty didn't know was that Alice did want to help, but she was just too scared of the bully.

Characters Succeed and Fail Conflict between characters, we see, is often between characters who love and *want* to understand each other, In Gish Jen's "The White Umbrella," the main character wishes she had a mother who loved her so much that she wouldn't work and would therefore always pick her up on time from her piano lessons. Actually, however, her mother loves

Literary Forms
Story

her so much that she's willing to take a job in a supermarket so she can *pay* for things like piano lessons.

In Toni Cade Bambara's story, "Raymond's Run," the narrator of the story discovers that she can appreciate even those people who challenge her status as fastest runner in the community. She finds that competition is a kind of conflict that can both break friendships apart and strengthen connections between people.

What Can Stories Teach? Some people scoff at stories, saying they can't teach us anything because they're "made up." I say that's not so. Characters live out a life on the printed page. Reading about them can tell us about ourselves and our relationships to other people. Just as all characters in some way try to figure out the meaning of life, we in turn can learn from their struggle.

Marie G. Lee (1964–   ) grew up in Hibbing, Minnesota, where she was the only Korean American in her high school. Before she went East to attend Brown University, she had already published one of her essays in *Seventeen* magazine. The title of that essay, "Volunteer Workers Get Paid Too," expressed a theme she has carried out in her life since then. She continues to volunteer at soup kitchens and homeless outreach programs.

A published author of several novels for young adults, she also teaches creative writing to sixth-graders through the New York City School Volunteers Program. She says that, for her, fiction writing is "wishing for what could have been."

Activities
PREVIEW
The White Umbrella by Gish Jen

How has a teacher or coach changed your life?

Reach Into Your Background

Has a good teacher or coach ever taught you to play a musical instrument, to sing, to dance, or to excel in a sport? What did that skill do for your image of yourself? Did you ever wish you could tell that teacher or coach how much what you had learned meant to you? Explore such an experience through one of the following activities:

- With a partner discuss teachers, instructors, or coaches you have known and how they have inspired you.
- List extracurricular activities or home-chore responsibilities that have taught you something important.

Read Actively
Identify Conflicts

As in real life, relationships between characters in stories do not always run smoothly. One person's words or actions can create a misunderstanding or hurt that, in turn, results in other problems. The struggle between characters is called a **conflict**. The conflict is the driving force behind the events in a story. In some stories, the conflict is **external**—between one character and another, for example; in others it is **internal**, within a character.

The character narrating "The White Umbrella," has concerns about what other people think. Her struggle with these concerns is an internal conflict that affects what she does, and therefore the way the story develops. As you read, list her concerns on a graphic like this one.

Narrator's concerns

The White Umbrella

Gish Jen

When I was twelve, my mother went to work without telling me or my little sister.

"Not that we need the second income." The lilt of her accent drifted from the kitchen up to the top of the stairs, where Mona and I were listening.

"No," said my father, in a barely audible voice. "Not like the Lee family."

The Lees were the only other Chinese family in town. I remembered how sorry my parents had felt for Mrs. Lee when she started waitressing downtown the year before; and so when my mother began coming home late, I didn't say anything, and tried to keep Mona from saying anything either.

"But why shouldn't I?" she argued. "Lots of people's mothers work."

"Those are American people," I said.

"So what do you think we are? I can do the pledge of allegiance with my eyes closed."

Nevertheless, she tried to be discreet; and if my mother wasn't home by 5:30, we would start cooking by ourselves, to make sure dinner would be on time. Mona would wash the vegetables and put on the rice; I would chop.

For weeks we wondered what kind of work she was doing. I imagined that she was selling perfume, testing dessert recipes for the local newspaper. Or maybe she was working for the florist. Now that she had learned to drive, she might be delivering boxes of roses to people.

"I don't think so," said Mona as we walked to our piano lesson after school. "She would've hit something by now."

A gust of wind littered the street with leaves.

"Maybe we better hurry up," she went on, looking at the sky. "It's going to pour."

"But we're too early." Her lesson didn't begin until 4:00, mine until 4:30, so we usually tried

Words to Know

audible (AW duh buhl) *adj.*: Able to be heard
allegiance (uh LEE juhns) *n.*: Loyalty

to walk as slowly as we could. "And anyway, those aren't the kind of clouds that rain. Those are cumulus clouds."

We arrived out of breath and wet.

"Oh, you poor, poor dears," said old Miss Crosman. "Why don't you call me the next time it's like this out? If your mother won't drive you, I can come pick you up."

"No, that's okay," I answered. Mona wrung her hair out on Miss Crosman's rug. "We just couldn't get the roof of our car to close, is all. We took it to the beach last summer and got sand in the mechanism." I pronounced this last word carefully, as if the credibility of my lie depended on its middle syllable. "It's never been the same." I thought for a second. "It's a convertible."

"Well then make yourselves at home." She exchanged looks with Eugenie Roberts, whose lesson we were interrupting. Eugenie smiled good-naturedly. "The towels are in the closet across from the bathroom."

Huddling at the end of Miss Crosman's nine-foot leatherette couch, Mona and I watched Eugenie play. She was a grade ahead of me and, according to school rumor, had a boyfriend in high school. I believed it. She had auburn hair, blue eyes, and, I noted with a particular pang, a pure white folding umbrella.

"I can't see," whispered Mona.

"So clean your glasses."

"My glasses *are* clean. You're in the way."

I looked at her. "They look dirty to me."

"That's because *your* glasses are dirty."

Eugenie came bouncing to the end of her piece.

"Oh! Just stupendous!" Miss Crosman hugged her, then looked up as Eugenie's mother walked in. "Stupendous!" she said again. "Oh! Mrs. Roberts! Your daughter has a gift, a real gift. It's an honor to teach her."

Mrs. Roberts, radiant with pride, swept her daughter out of the room as if she were royalty, born to the piano bench. Watching the way Eugenie carried herself, I sat up, and concentrated so hard on sucking in my stomach that I did not realize until the Robertses were gone that Eugenie had left her umbrella.

As Mona began to play, I jumped up and ran to the window, meaning to call to them—only to see their brake lights flash then fade at the stop sign at the corner. As if to allow them passage, the rain had let up; a quivering sun lit their way.

The umbrella glowed like a scepter on the blue carpet while Mona, slumping over the keyboard, managed to eke out a fair rendition of a catfight. At the end of the piece, Miss Crosman asked her to stand up.

"Stay right there," she said, then came back a minute later with a towel to cover the bench. "You must be cold," she continued. "Shall I call your mother and have her bring over some dry clothes?"

"No," answered Mona. "She won't come because she . . ."

"She's too busy," I broke in from the back of the room.

"I see." Miss Crosman sighed and shook her head a little. "Your glasses are filthy, honey," she said to Mona. "Shall I clean them for you?"

Sisterly embarrassment seized me. Why hadn't Mona wiped her lenses when I told her to? As she resumed abuse of the piano, I stared at the umbrella. I wanted to open it, twirl it around by its slender silver handle; I wanted to dangle it from my wrist on the way to school the way the other girls did. I wondered what Miss Crosman would say if I offered to bring it to Eugenie at school tomorrow. She would be impressed with my consideration for others; Eugenie would be pleased to have it back; and I would have possession of the umbrella for an entire night. I looked at it again, toying with the idea of asking for one for Christmas. I knew, however, how my mother would react.

"Things," she would say. "What's the mat-

Words to Know

credibility (kred uh BIL i tee) *n.*: Believability
syllable (SIL uh buhl) *n.*: One of the parts into which a word is divided
radiant (RAY dee uhnt) *adj.*: Shining brightly

ter with a raincoat? All you want is things, just like an American."

Sitting down for my lesson, I was careful to keep the towel under me and sit up straight.

"I'll bet you can't see a thing either," said Miss Crosman, reaching for my glasses. "And you can relax, you poor dear." She touched my chest, in an area where she never would have touched Eugenie Roberts. "This isn't a boot camp."

When Miss Crosman finally allowed me to start playing I played extra well, as well as I possibly could. See, I told her with my fingers. You don't have to feel sorry for me.

"That was wonderful," said Miss Crosman. "Oh! Just wonderful."

An entire constellation rose in my heart.

"And guess what," I announced proudly. "I have a surprise for you."

Then I played a second piece for her, a much more difficult one that she had not assigned.

"Oh! That was stupendous," she said without hugging me. "Stupendous! You are a genius, young lady. If your mother had started you younger, you'd be playing like Eugenie Roberts by now!"

I looked at the keyboard, wishing that I had still a third, even more difficult piece to play for her. I wanted to tell her that I was the school spelling bee champion, that I wasn't ticklish, that I could do karate.

"My mother is a concert pianist," I said.

She looked at me for a long moment, then finally, without saying anything, hugged me. I didn't say anything about bringing the umbrella to Eugenie at school.

The steps were dry when Mona and I sat down to wait for my mother.

"Do you want to wait inside?" Miss Crosman looked anxiously at the sky.

"No," I said. "Our mother will be here any minute."

"In a while," said Mona.

"Any minute," I said again, even though my mother had been at least twenty minutes late every week since she started working.

According to the church clock across the

Words to Know

constellation (kahn stuh LAY shuhn) *n.*: A cluster of stars

street we had been waiting twenty-five minutes when Miss Crosman came out again.

"Shall I give you ladies a ride home?"

"No," I said. "Our mother is coming any minute."

"Shall I at least give her a call and remind her you're here? Maybe she forgot about you."

"I don't think she *forgot*," said Mona.

"Shall I give her a call anyway? Just to be safe?"

"I bet she already left," I said. "How could she forget about us?"

Miss Crosman went in to call.

"There's no answer," she said, coming back out.

"See, she's on her way," I said.

"Are you sure you wouldn't like to come in?"

"No," said Mona.

"Yes," I said. I pointed at my sister. "She meant yes too. She meant no, she wouldn't like to go in."

Miss Crosman looked at her watch. "It's 5:30 now, ladies. My pot roast will be coming out in fifteen minutes. Maybe you'd like to come in and have some then?"

"My mother's almost here," I said. "She's on her way."

We watched and watched the street. I tried to imagine what my mother was doing; I tried to imagine her writing messages in the sky, even though I knew she was afraid of planes. I watched as the branches of Miss Crosman's big willow tree started to sway;

Girl in Car Window Winson Trang, Courtesy of the artist

they had all been trimmed to exactly the same height off the ground, so that they looked beautiful, like hair in the wind.

It started to rain.

"Miss Crosman is coming out again," said Mona.

"Don't let her talk you into going inside," I whispered.

"Why not?"

"Because that would mean Mom isn't really coming any minute."

"But she isn't," said Mona. "She's *working*."

"Shhh! Miss Crosman is going to hear you."

"She's working! She's working! She's working!"

I put my hand over her mouth, but she licked it, and so I was wiping my hand on my wet dress when the front door opened.

"We're getting even *wetter*," said Mona right away. "Wetter and wetter."

"Shall we all go in?" Miss Crosman pulled Mona to her feet. "Before you young ladies catch pneumonia? You've been out half an hour already."

"We're *freezing*." Mona looked up at Miss Crosman. "Do you have any hot chocolate? We're going to catch *pneumonia*."

"I'm not going in," I said. "My mother's coming any minute."

Words to Know

pneumonia (noo MOHN yuh) *n.*: A serious infection of the lungs

"Come on," said Mona. "Use your *noggin*."[1]

"Any minute."

"Come on, Mona," Miss Crosman opened the door. "Shall we get you inside first?"

"See you in the hospital," said Mona as she went in. "See you in the hospital with *pneumonia*."

I stared out into the empty street. The rain was pricking me all over; I was cold; I wanted to go inside. I wanted to be able to let myself go inside. If Miss Crosman came out again, I decided, I would go in.

She came out with a blanket and the white umbrella.

I could not believe that I was actually holding the umbrella, opening it. It sprang up by itself as if it were alive, as if that were what it wanted to do—as if it belonged in my hands, above my head. I stared up at the network of silver spokes, then spun the umbrella around and around and around. It was so clean and white that it seemed to glow, to illuminate everything around it.

"It's beautiful," I said.

Miss Crosman sat down next to me, on one end of the blanket. I moved the umbrella over so that it covered that too. I could feel the rain on my left shoulder and shivered. She put her arm around me.

"You poor, poor dear."

I knew that I was in store for another bolt of sympathy, and braced myself by staring up into the umbrella.

"You know, I very much wanted to have children when I was younger," she continued.

"You did?"

She stared at me a minute. Her face looked dry and crusty, like day-old frosting.

"I did. But then I never got married."

I twirled the umbrella around again.

"This is the most beautiful umbrella I have ever seen," I said. "Ever, in my whole life."

"Do you have an umbrella?"

"No. But my mother's going to get me one just like this for Christmas."

"Is she? I tell you what. You don't have to wait until Christmas. You can have this one."

"But this one belongs to Eugenie Roberts," I protested. "I have to give it back to her tomorrow in school."

"Who told you it belongs to Eugenie? It's not Eugenie's. It's mine. And now I'm giving it to you, so it's yours."

"It is?"

She hugged me tighter. "That's right. It's all yours."

"It's mine?" I didn't know what to say. "Mine?" Suddenly I was jumping up and down in the rain. "It's beautiful! Oh! It's beautiful!" I laughed.

Miss Crosman laughed too, even though she was getting all wet.

"Thank you, Miss Crosman. Thank you very much. Thanks a zillion. It's beautiful. It's *stupendous!*"

"You're quite welcome," she said.

"Thank you," I said again, but that didn't seem like enough. Suddenly I knew just what she wanted to hear. "I wish you were my mother."

Right away I felt bad.

"You shouldn't say that," she said, but her face was opening into a huge smile as the lights of my mother's car cautiously turned the corner. I quickly collapsed the umbrella and put it up my skirt, holding onto it from the outside, through the material.

"Mona!" I shouted into the house. "Mona! Hurry up! Mom's here! I told you she was coming!"

Then I ran away from Miss Crosman, down to the curb. Mona came tearing up to my side as my mother neared the house. We both backed up a few feet, so that in case she went onto the curb, she wouldn't run us over.

"But why didn't you go inside with Mona?" my mother asked on the way home. She had taken off her own coat to put over me, and had the heat on high.

"She wasn't using her noggin," said Mona, next to me in the back seat.

"I should call next time," said my mother. "I just don't like to say where I am."

That was when she finally told us that she was working as a check-out clerk in the A&P. She was supposed to be on the day

---

1. noggin (NAHG uhn) *n*.: Slang for head or brain.

shift, but the other employees were unreliable, and her boss had promised her a promotion if she would stay until the evening shift filled in.

For a moment no one said anything. Even Mona seemed to find the revelation disappointing.

"A promotion already!" she said, finally.

I listened to the windshield wipers.

"You're so quiet." My mother looked at me in the rear view mirror. "What's the matter?"

"I wish you would quit," I said after a moment.

She sighed. "The Chinese have a saying: one beam cannot hold the roof up."

"But Eugenie Roberts's father supports their family."

She sighed once more. "Eugenie Roberts's father is Eugenie Roberts's father," she said.

As we entered the downtown area, Mona started leaning hard against me every time the car turned right, trying to push me over. Remembering what I had said to Miss Crosman, I tried to maneuver the umbrella under my leg so she wouldn't feel it.

"What's under your skirt?" Mona wanted to know as we came to a traffic light. My mother, watching us in the rear view mirror again, rolled slowly to a stop.

"What's the matter?" she asked.

"There's something under her skirt!" said Mona, pulling at me.

"Under her skirt?"

Meanwhile, a man crossing the street started to yell at us. "Who do you think you are, lady?" he said. "You're blocking the whole crosswalk."

We all froze. Other people walking by stopped to watch.

"Didn't you hear me?" he went on, starting to thump on the hood with his fist. "Don't you speak English?"

My mother began to back up, but the car behind us honked. Luckily, the light turned green right after that. She sighed in relief.

"What were you saying, Mona?" she asked.

We wouldn't have hit the car behind us that hard if he hadn't been moving too, but as it was our car bucked violently, throwing us all first back and then forward.

"Uh oh," said Mona when we stopped. "*Another* accident."

I was relieved to have attention diverted from the umbrella. Then I noticed my mother's head, tilted back onto the seat. Her eyes were closed.

"Mom!" I screamed. "Mom! Wake up!"

She opened her eyes. "Please don't yell," she said. "Enough people are going to yell already."

"I thought you were dead," I said, starting to cry. "I thought you were dead."

She turned around, looked at me intently, then put her hand to my forehead.

"Sick," she confirmed. "Some kind of sick is giving you crazy ideas."

As the man from the car behind us started tapping on the window, I moved the umbrella away from my leg. Then Mona and my mother were getting out of the car. I got out after them; and while everyone else was inspecting the damage we'd done, I threw the umbrella down a sewer.

Respond

- What advice would you give to the narrator about the white umbrella?
- How can people make amends for things they regret saying?

Gish Jen (1956–   )

Q: Where did Gish Jen get her unusual first name?

A: Named Lillian, she was nicknamed Gish after the actress Lillian Gish.

Q: What was Gish Jen's childhood like?

A: The daughter of Chinese immigrants, Jen grew up outside of New York City, where she and her family were the only Asian Americans in the area. She recalls, "People threw things at us and called us names. We thought it was normal."

Q: What is Gish Jen's goal as a writer?

A: Jen says, "If there is one thing I hope readers come away with, it is to see Asian Americans as 'us' rather than 'other.'"

Activities
MAKE MEANING

Explore Your Reading

Look Back (Recall)

1. Why do the girls stay so late at their music lesson?

Think It Over (Interpret)

2. Why does the narrator not tell Miss Crosman the truth about why her mother is late?
3. Why is the umbrella important to the narrator?
4. Why does the narrator throw the umbrella in the sewer?

Go Beyond (Apply)

5. The narrator and her mother are very aware of being different from "Americans." How does feeling that you are different make it harder to be yourself with other people?

Develop Reading and Literary Skills

Analyze Conflict in Plot

All short stories center on one or more conflicts. As you see in "The White Umbrella," the narrator's **internal conflicts** bring about the events in the story, its **plot**. For example, her wish to conceal from her piano teacher the fact that her mother works makes her wait outside in the rain, and results in the gift of the white umbrella. The umbrella, in turn, sets up another conflict, which she tries to hide from her mother.

1. List each of the internal conflicts you identified in the story.
2. Which is the central conflict?
3. Is the central conflict resolved, or settled, in the story? Explain.

Ideas for Writing

As in "The White Umbrella," a person's response to conflict affects his or her relationships with other people.

Analysis of Conflict The narrator in "The White Umbrella" has several conflicts. Identify one of her conflicts and write an essay explaining what happens as a result of that conflict. Explain how the conflict is resolved and whether or not you are satisfied with the resolution.

What-if Story Write a different ending for "The White Umbrella" in which the narrator keeps the umbrella instead of throwing it away. Your new ending should make it clear why she keeps the umbrella and how her decision affects her life at home.

Ideas for Projects

Recording The narrator is proud of her accomplishment in music. Choose a recording of a musical artist—a singer, violinist, pianist, or clarinetist, for example—whose expression you really admire. Play the recording for a group of your classmates and explain the qualities of musical expression that you admire in it. [Music Link]

Poster Display Make a poster of different people who have influenced you and shaped your interests. Use photographs, magazine and newspaper clippings, and drawings. Write notes to the most important people in your poster, thanking them for what they added to your life.

How Am I Doing?

Write brief responses in your journal to these questions:

How will my understanding of conflict help me read other stories?

Which piece of my work shows my understanding of conflict?

What accomplishment are you most proud of?

Reach Into Your Background

Most of us have had experiences with competition—athletic, talent, or academic. What kind(s) of competition do you enjoy? Have you ever felt that you just *had* to win a particular contest? Think about what you did to prepare for it, and what the outcome was.

- In a small group, discuss the benefits and downsides of competing.
- Role-play a friendly competition, such as thumbwrestling, with a partner. Compare how it feels to win and to lose.

Read Actively

Observe a Narrator's Viewpoint

How do you think a competitive attitude would affect a character's point of view? When a storyteller, or **narrator**, is an actual character in the story and gives you his or her firsthand account of people and events, that is called **first-person point of view**. Squeaky is such a narrator in "Raymond's Run."

A first-person narrator's version of a story excites your interest, because the narrator has a personal stake in what happens in the story. However, you need to remember that first-person narrators give their own interpretations of events and people.

As you read this story, pay attention to what you learn about the first-person narrator, Squeaky, from the way she sees other people and events. Make a double-entry journal like this one to list the most striking details—her own comments and those she reports by other people—that reveal her personality, concerns, and attitudes.

Squeaky's comment or thought	What it shows about her

Raymond's Run

Toni Cade Bambara

I don't have much work to do around the house like some girls. My mother does that. And I don't have to earn my pocket money by hustling; George runs errands for the big boys and sells Christmas cards. And anything else that's got to get done, my father does. All I have to do in life is mind my brother Raymond, which is enough.

Sometimes I slip and say my little brother Raymond. But as any fool can see he's much bigger and he's older too. But a lot of people call him my little brother cause he needs looking after cause he's not quite right. And a lot of smart mouths got lots to say about that too, especially when George was minding him. But now, if anybody has anything to say to Raymond, anything to say about his big head, they have to come by me. And I don't play the dozens[1] or believe in standing around with somebody in my face doing a lot of talking. I much rather just knock you down and take my chances even if I am a lit-

📖 **Read Actively**

Visualize how Squeaky and her brother Raymond look from the descriptions she gives here.

tle girl with skinny arms and a squeaky voice, which is how I got the name Squeaky. And if things get too rough, I run. And as anybody can tell you, I'm the fastest thing on two feet.

There is no track meet that I don't win the first place medal. I used to win the twenty-yard dash when I was a little kid in kindergarten. Nowadays, it's the fifty-yard dash. And tomorrow I'm subject to run the quarter-meter relay all by myself and come in first, second, and third. The big kids call me Mercury[2] cause I'm the swiftest thing in the neighborhood. Everybody knows that—except two people who know better, my father and me. He can beat me to Amsterdam Avenue with me having a two fire-hydrant headstart and him running with his hands in his pockets and whistling. But that's private information. Cause can you imagine some thirty-five-year-old man stuffing himself into PAL[3] shorts to race little kids? So as far as everyone's concerned, I'm the fastest and that goes for Gretchen, too, who has put out the tale that she is going to win the first-place medal this year. Ridiculous. In the second place, she's got short legs. In the third place, she's got freckles. In the first place, no one can beat me and that's all there is to it.

I'm standing on the corner admiring the weather and about to take a stroll down Broadway so I can practice my breathing exercises, and I've got Raymond walking on the inside close to the buildings, cause he's subject to fits of fantasy and starts thinking he's a circus performer and that the curb is a tightrope strung high in the air. And sometimes after a rain he likes to step down off his tightrope right into the gutter and slosh around getting his shoes and cuffs wet. Then I get hit when I get home. Or sometimes if you don't watch him he'll dash across traffic to the island in the middle of Broadway and give the pigeons a fit. Then I have to go behind him apologizing to all the old people

---

1. **the dozens**: A game in which the players insult one another; the first to show anger loses.

2. **Mercury:** In Roman mythology, the messenger of the gods, known for great speed.

3. **PAL:** Police Athletic League.

sitting around trying to get some sun and getting all upset with the pigeons fluttering around them, scattering their newspapers and upsetting the waxpaper lunches in their laps. So I keep Raymond on the inside of me, and he plays like he's driving a stage coach which is O.K. by me so long as he doesn't run me over or interrupt my breathing exercises, which I have to do on

📖 **Read Actively**

Connect with Squeaky's feelings toward her brother. Have you ever felt protective toward another person?

say something like, "Oh, I guess I'll play handball this afternoon and watch television tonight," just to let you know she ain't thinking about the test. Or like last week when she won the spelling bee for the millionth time, "A good thing you got 'receive,' Squeaky, cause I would have got it wrong. I completely forgot about the spelling bee." And she'll clutch the lace on her blouse like it was a narrow escape. Oh, brother. But of course when I pass her house on my early morning trots around the block, she is practicing the scales on the piano over and over and over and over. Then in music class she always lets herself get bumped around so she falls accidently on purpose onto the piano stool and is so surprised to find herself sitting there that she decides just for fun to try out the ole keys. And what do you know—Chopin's[4] waltzes just spring out of her fingertips and she's the most surprised thing in the world. A regular prodigy. I could kill people like that. I

account of I'm serious about my running, and I don't care who knows it.

Now some people like to act like things come easy to them, won't let on that they practice. Not me. I'll high-prance down 34th Street like a rodeo pony to keep my knees strong even if it does get my mother uptight so that she walks ahead like she's not with me, don't know me, is all by herself on a shopping trip, and I am somebody else's crazy child. Now you take Cynthia Procter for instance. She's just the opposite. If there's a test tomorrow, she'll

stay up all night studying the words for the spelling bee. And you can see me any time of day practicing running. I never walk if I can trot, and shame on Raymond if he can't keep up. But of course he does, cause if he hangs back someone's liable to walk up to him and get smart, or take his allowance from him, or ask him where he got that great big pumpkin head. People are so stupid sometimes.

---

4. Chopin (sho PAHN): Frédéric François Chopin (1810–1849), Polish composer and pianist.

So I'm strolling down Broadway breathing out and breathing in on counts of seven, which is my lucky number, and here comes Gretchen and her sidekicks: Mary Louise, who used to be a friend of mine when she first moved to Harlem from Baltimore and got beat up by everybody till I took up for her on account of her mother and my mother used to sing in the same choir when they were young girls, but people ain't grateful, so now she hangs out with the new girl Gretchen and talks about me like a dog; and Rosie, who is as fat as I am skinny and has a big mouth where Raymond is concerned and is too stupid to know that there is not a big deal of difference between herself and Raymond and that she can't afford to throw stones. So they are steady coming up Broadway and I see right away that it's going to be one of those Dodge City[5] scenes cause the street ain't that big and they're close to the buildings just as we are. First I think I'll step into the candy store and look over the new comics and let them pass. But that's chicken and I've got a reputation to consider. So then I think I'll just walk straight on through them or even over them if necessary. But as they get to me, they slow down. I'm ready to fight, cause like I said I don't feature a whole lot of chit-chat, I much prefer to just knock you down right from the jump and save everybody a lotta precious time.

📖 **Read Actively**

Question how emotionally involved Squeaky is in her story.

"You signing up for the May Day races?" smiles Mary Louise, only it's not a smile at all. A dumb question like that doesn't deserve an answer. Besides, there's just me and Gretchen standing there really, so no use wasting my breath talking to shadows.

---

5. Dodge City: The location of the television program *Gunsmoke*, which often presented a gunfight between the sheriff and an outlaw.

"I don't think you're going to win this time," says Rosie, trying to signify with her hands on her hips all salty, completely forgetting that I have whupped her behind many times for less salt than that.

"I always win cause I'm the best," I say straight at Gretchen who is, as far as I'm concerned, the only one talking in this ventriloquist-dummy routine. Gretchen smiles, but it's not a smile, and I'm thinking that girls never really smile at each other because they don't know how and don't want to know how and there's probably no one to teach us how, cause grownup girls don't know either. Then they all look at Raymond who has just brought his mule team to a standstill. And they're about to see what trouble they can get into through him.

"What grade you in now, Raymond?"

"You got anything to say to my brother, you say it to me, Mary Louise Williams of Raggedy Town, Baltimore."

"What are you, his mother?" sasses Rosie.

"That's right, Fatso. And the next word out of anybody and I'll be *their* mother too." So they just stand there and Gretchen shifts from one leg to the other and so do they. Then Gretchen puts her hands on her hips and is about to say something with her freckle-face self but doesn't. Then she walks around me looking me up and down but keeps walking up Broadway, and her sidekicks follow her. So me and Raymond smile at each other and he says, "Gidyap" to his team and I continue with

Words to Know

prance (PRANS) *v.*: Hop around

prodigy (PRAHD uh jee) *n.*: A wonder; an unusually talented person

reputation (rep yoo TAY shuhn) *n.*: What other people think about someone

ventriloquist (ven TRIL uh kwist) *n.*: Someone who speaks through a puppet or dummy

my breathing exercises, strolling down Broadway toward the ice man on 145th with not a care in the world cause I am Miss Quicksilver herself.

I take my time getting to the park on May Day because the track meet is the last thing on the program. The biggest thing on the program is the May Pole dancing, which I can do without, thank you, even if my mother thinks it's a shame I don't take part and act like a girl for a change. You'd think my mother'd be grateful not to have to make me a white organdy dress with a big satin sash and buy me new white baby-doll shoes that can't be taken out of the box till the big day. You'd think she'd be glad her daughter ain't out there prancing around a May Pole getting the new clothes all dirty and sweaty and trying to act like a fairy or a flower or whatever you're supposed to be when you should be trying to be yourself, whatever that is, which is, as far as I am concerned, a poor black girl who really can't afford to buy shoes and a new dress you only wear once a lifetime cause it won't fit next year.

I was once a strawberry in a Hansel and Gretel pageant when I was in nursery school and didn't have no better sense than to dance on tiptoe with my arms in a circle over my head doing umbrella steps and being a perfect fool just so my mother and father could come dressed up and clap. You'd think they'd know better than to encourage that kind of nonsense. I am not a strawberry. I do not dance on my toes. I run. That is what I am all about. So I always come late to the May Day program, just in time to get my number pinned on and lay in the grass till they announce the fifty-yard dash.

Words to Know

periscope (PER uh skohp) *n*.: An instrument containing mirrors and lenses to see objects not in a direct line from the viewer; often used in submarines to see objects above the water

I put Raymond in the little swings, which is a tight squeeze this year and will be impossible next year. Then I look around for Mr. Pearson, who pins the numbers on. I'm really looking for Gretchen if you want to know the truth, but she's not around. The park is jam-packed. Parents in hats and corsages and breast-pocket handkerchiefs peeking up. Kids in white dresses and light-blue suits. The parkees unfolding chairs and chasing the rowdy kids from Lenox as if they had no right to be there. The big guys with their caps on backwards, leaning against the fence swirling the basketballs on the tips of their fingers, waiting for all these crazy people to clear out the park so they can play. Most of the kids in my class are carrying bass drums and glockenspiels[6] and flutes. You'd think they'd put in a few bongos or something for real like that.

Then here comes Mr. Pearson with his clipboard and his cards and pencils and whistles and safety pins and fifty million other things he's always dropping all over the place with his clumsy self. He sticks out in a crowd because he's on stilts. We used to call him Jack and the Beanstalk to get him mad. But I'm the only one that can outrun him and get away, and I'm too grown for that silliness now.

"Well, Squeaky," he says, checking my name off the list and handing me number seven and two pins. And I'm thinking he's got no right to call me Squeaky, if I can't call him Beanstalk.

"Hazel Elizabeth Deborah Parker," I correct him and tell him to write it down on his board.

"Well, Hazel Elizabeth Deborah Parker, going to give someone else a break this year?" I squint at him real hard to see if he is seriously thinking I should lose the race on purpose just to give someone else a break. "Only six girls running this time,"

---

6. **glockenspiels** (GLOK uhn speelz) *n*.: Musical instruments with flat metal bars that make bell-like tones when struck.

he continues, shaking his head sadly like it's my fault all of New York didn't turn out in sneakers. "That new girl should give you a run for your money." He looks around the park for Gretchen like a periscope in a submarine movie. "Wouldn't it be a nice gesture if you were . . . to ahhh . . ."

I give him such a look he couldn't finish putting that idea into words. Grownups got a lot of nerve sometimes. I pin number seven to myself and stomp away, I'm so burnt. And I go straight for the track and stretch out on the grass while the band winds up with "Oh, the Monkey Wrapped His Tail Around the Flag Pole," which my teacher calls by some other name. The man on the loudspeaker is calling everyone over to the track and I'm on my back looking at the sky, trying to pretend I'm in the country, but I can't, because even grass in the city feels hard as sidewalk, and there's just no pretending you are anywhere but in a "concrete jungle" as my grandfather says.

The twenty-yard dash takes all of two minutes cause most of the little kids don't know no better than to run off the track or run the wrong way or run smack into the fence and fall down and cry. One little kid, though, has got the good sense to run straight for the white ribbon up ahead, so he wins. Then the second-graders line up for the thirty-yard dash and I don't even bother to turn my head to watch cause Raphael Perez always wins. He wins before he even begins by psyching[7] the runners, telling them they're going to trip on their shoelaces and fall on their faces or lose their shorts or something, which he doesn't really have to do since he is very

fast, almost as fast as I am. After that is the forty-yard dash which I use to run when I was in first grade. Raymond is hollering from the swings cause he knows I'm about to do my thing cause the man on the loudspeaker has just announced the fifty-yard dash, although he might just as well be giving a recipe for angel food cake cause you can hardly make out what he's sayin for the static. I get up and slip off my sweat

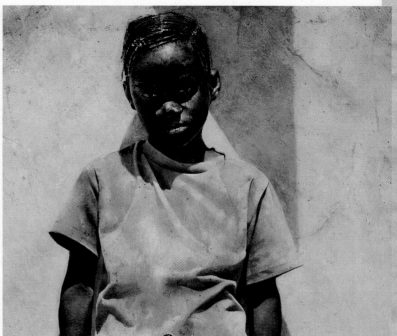

Green Eyes, 1988 (detail)
Stephen Scott Young, John H. Surovek Gallery, Palm Beach, Florida

pants and then I see Gretchen standing at the starting line, kicking her legs out like a pro. Then as I get into place I see that ole Raymond is on line on the other side of the fence, bending down with his fingers on the ground just like he knew what he was doing. I was going to yell at him but then I didn't. It burns up your energy to holler.

Every time, just before I take off in a race, I always feel like I'm in a dream, the kind of dream you have when you're sick with fever and feel all hot and weightless. I dream I'm flying over a sandy beach in the early morning sun, kissing the leaves of

---

7. psyching (SĪ king) *v.*: Slang for playing on a person's mental state.

the trees as I fly by. And there's always the smell of apples, just like in the country when I was little and used to think I was a choo-choo train, running through the fields of corn and chugging up the hill to the orchard. And all the time I'm dreaming this, I get lighter and lighter until I'm flying over the beach again, getting blown through the sky like a feather that weighs nothing at all. But once I spread my fin-

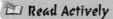 **Read Actively**

Connect with Squeaky's point of view when she races. How do you feel during a competition?

crunch as I zoom over the gravel in the track. I glance to my left and there is no one. To the right, a blurred Gretchen, who's got her chin jutting out as if it would win the race all by itself. And on the other side of the fence is Raymond with his arms down to his side and the palms

tucked up behind him, running in his very own style, and it's the first time I ever saw that and I almost stop to watch my brother Raymond on his first run. But the white ribbon is bouncing toward me and I tear past it, racing into the distance till my feet with a mind of their own start digging up footfuls of dirt and brake me short. Then all the kids standing on the side pile on me, banging me on the back and slapping my head with their May Day programs, for I have won again and everybody on 151st Street can walk tall for another year.

"In first place . . ." the man on the loudspeaker is clear as a bell now. But then he pauses and the loudspeaker starts to whine.

gers in the dirt and crouch over the Get on Your Mark, the dream goes and I am solid again and am telling myself, Squeaky you must win, you must win, you are the fastest thing in the world, you can even beat your father up Amsterdam if you really try. And then I feel my weight coming back just behind my knees then down to my feet then into the earth and the pistol shot explodes in my blood and I am off and weightless again, flying past the other runners, my arms pumping up and down and the whole world is quiet except for the

Then static. And I lean down to catch my breath and here comes Gretchen walking back, for she's overshot the finish line too, huffing and puffing with her hands on her hips taking it slow, breathing in steady time like a real pro and I sort of like her a little for the first time. "In first place . . ." and then three or four voices get all mixed up on the loudspeaker and I dig my sneaker into the grass and stare at Gretchen who's staring back, we both wondering just who did win. I can hear old Beanstalk arguing with the man on the loudspeaker and then a few others running their mouths about what the stopwatches say. Then I hear Raymond yanking at the fence to call me and I wave to shush him, but he keeps rattling the fence like a gorilla in a cage like in them gorilla movies, but then like a dancer or something he starts climbing up nice and easy but very fast. And it occurs to me, watching how smoothly he climbs hand over hand and remembering how he looked running with his arms down to his side and with the wind pulling his mouth back and his teeth showing and all, it occurred to me that Raymond would make a very fine runner. Doesn't he always keep up with me on my trots? And he surely knows how to breathe in counts of seven cause he's always doing it at the dinner table, which drives my brother George up the wall. And I'm smiling to beat the band cause if I've lost this race, or if me and Gretchen tied, or even if I've won, I can always retire as a runner and begin a whole new career as a coach with Raymond as my champion. After all, with a little more study I can beat Cynthia and her phony self at the spelling bee. And if I bugged my mother, I could get piano lessons and become a star. And I have a big rep as the baddest thing around. And I've got a roomful of ribbons and medals and awards. But what has Raymond got to call his own?

So I stand there with my new plans, laughing out loud by this time as Raymond jumps down from the fence and runs over with his teeth showing and his arms down to the side, which no one before him has quite mastered as a running style. And by the time he comes over I'm jumping up and down so glad to see him—my brother Raymond, a great runner in the family tradition. But of course everyone thinks I'm jumping up and down because the men on the loudspeaker have finally gotten themselves together and compared notes and are announcing "In first place—Miss Hazel Elizabeth Deborah Parker." (Dig that.) "In

📖 Read Actively

Predict how Squeaky will be different in her treatment of Gretchen in the future.

second place—Miss Gretchen P. Lewis." And I look over at Gretchen wondering what the "P" stands for. And I smile. Cause she's good, no doubt about it. Maybe she'd like to help me coach Raymond; she obviously is serious about running, as any fool can see. And she nods to congratulate me and then she smiles. And I smile. We stand there with this big smile of respect between us. It's about as real a smile as girls can do for each other, considering we don't practice real smiling every day, you know, cause maybe we too busy being flowers or fairies or strawberries instead of something honest and worthy of respect . . . you know . . . like being people.

Respond

- What do you like about Squeaky? What wouldn't you like about her if she were someone you knew?
- Has your view of competition changed as a result of reading this story? Explain.

Toni Cade Bambara

(1939–   ) Here is what a critic wrote in *The New York Times Book Review* about Toni Cade Bambara's concern for other people as expressed in her writing: "Bambara tells me more about being black through her quiet, proud, silly, tender, hip, acute, loving stories than any amount of literary [discussion] could hope to do. . . . All of her stories share the affection that their narrator feels for the subject, an affection that is sometimes terribly painful, at other times fiercely proud."

Activities

MAKE MEANING

Explore Your Reading

Look Back (Recall)

1. Why does Squeaky have to take special care of Raymond?
2. What does Raymond do when Squeaky runs her race?

Think It Over (Interpret)

3. What do Squeaky's statements about Raymond reveal about her?
4. What are some of the pros and cons of competing that Squeaky reveals in her story?
5. What does the final sentence of the story mean?

Go Beyond (Apply)

6. Is being as committed to winning as Squeaky is a positive attribute or not? Explain.

Develop Reading and Literary Skills

Appreciate a First-Person Narrator

When you read a story narrated in the **first person** like "Raymond's Run," you learn what that narrator is like directly from what she tells you. You also learn about the narrator's attitudes toward the other characters and events. In fact, the narrator's attitude colors the way in which other characters and events are presented.

Analyze how Squeaky's point of view influences the information she presents in the story.

1. Choose two quotations and details from your double-entry journal that show Squeaky's attitude.
2. Explain how Squeaky's point of view affects her description of the race.
3. Sum up Squeaky's character, based on what her views reveal about her.

Ideas for Writing

Squeaky's viewpoint is strongly competitive. Explore other viewpoints in the following writing activities.

Story Retelling Retell the story from Gretchen's or Raymond's point of view, using first-person narration. Think about how this new point of view will differ from Squeaky's. How does this narrator feel about Squeaky? What does the new narrator know that Squeaky does not? Write consistently in a voice that suits your new narrator.

Evaluate Competition Write an essay discussing the pros and cons of competition. Back up your opinions with quotations and examples from the story and from your own experience.

Ideas for Projects

Oral Report Choose an athlete or other public figure who has written a short autobiography. Also find a short biography or article about him or her. Compare the two accounts and identify any differences that you discover. Present an oral report of your findings to the class.

Panel Discussion With a group, research the Special Olympics—its history, participants, funding, and current status. Organize the information you gather and hold a panel discussion to share it with the class. Record your discussion to help you evaluate its effectiveness.

How Am I Doing?

Jot a response to these questions:

How will what I've learned about first-person narrators help me read other stories?

Which of the activities or projects that I've done might I include in my portfolio? Why?

How Do I Relate to Others?

Student Art *Me, Twice Lit in the Shadows*
Neng Her
Kosciuszko Middle School, Milwaukee, Wisconsin

 **Student Writing,** *Anonymous*
Creative Learning Community, District 4 Public School, New York, New York

What started out as a mere hello
  Was the seed of friendship that began to grow
Before it blossomed, I knew it would be
  Something so special that only we'd see
That beam of sunlight helped
  Show us the way

To the gift of friendship that we share
  today
  And so, my friend, what I say is true
From now and always, I will forever love
  you.

What can a person do to fix a troubling relationship?

Reach Into Your Background

When people have misunderstandings with others, they usually try to resolve them. Sometimes they have to use different approaches with different people. For example, it might be more difficult to resolve a problem when the people who disagree are of very different ages.

- With a partner, role-play a situation in which you resolve a disagreement in a constructive way.
- In a group, brainstorm to develop a list of strategies for resolving conflicts.

Read Actively
Make Inferences

A misunderstanding or problem and the way it is worked out are often at the heart of a folk tale, a story that has been retold from generation to generation. In order to understand the message of a folk tale, you note the words, actions, thoughts, and responses of the characters and make **inferences,** or logical guesses, about information not stated explicitly.

As you read this folk tale, list each character in your journal and jot down a few ideas about each. For example, when the old grandfather drops his food dish, you could infer that he is weak and that his eyesight is failing.

Remembrance (Erinnerung), Ca. 1918
Marc Chagall
Solomon R. Guggenheim Museum

The Old Grandfather and His Little Grandson

Leo Tolstoy

The grandfather had become very old. His legs would not carry him, his eyes could not see, his ears could not hear, and he was toothless. When he ate, bits of food sometimes dropped out of his mouth. His son and his son's wife no longer allowed him to eat with them at the table. He had to eat his meals in the corner near the stove.

One day they gave him his food in a bowl. He tried to move the bowl closer; it fell to the floor and broke. His daughter-in-law scolded him. She told him that he spoiled everything in the house and broke their dishes, and she said

Words to Know

scolded (SKOHLD ed) *v.*: Criticized in a harsh way

that from now on he would get his food in a wooden dish. The old man sighed and said nothing.

A few days later, the old man's son and his wife were sitting in their hut, resting and watching their little boy playing on the floor. They saw him putting together something out of small pieces of wood. His father asked him, "What are you making, Misha?"

The little grandson said, "I'm making a wooden bucket. When you and Mamma get old, I'll feed you out of this wooden dish."

The young peasant and his wife looked at each other, and tears filled their eyes. They were ashamed because they had treated the old grandfather so meanly, and from that day they again let the old man eat with them at the table and took better care of him.

Words to Know

meanly (MEEN lee) *adv.*: Unkindly

Respond

Do you agree that children can teach grownups as the little grandson does? Explain.

Leo Tolstoy (1828–1900)
After Leo Tolstoy's parents died when he was a child, he was raised by relatives and educated by foreign tutors. As a boy, Tolstoy's favorite things to read were the folk tales of his native Russia, poems about ancient Russian heroes, and stories from the Bible. By the time he was ten, he began writing his own versions of fables and stories.

As a teenager, Tolstoy pondered questions of good and evil, right and wrong—and he eventually became deeply religious. "We search for . . . goodness, perfection in all this," he wrote in his diary, "but perfection is not given to man in anything."

Activities
MAKE MEANING

Explore Your Reading

Look Back (Recall)

1. What does the grandson say when his father asks what he's doing?

Think It Over (Interpret)

2. Why might the man and his wife reasonably be annoyed with the old grandfather during the first part of the tale?
3. Why does the grandson assume that he should imitate his parents' behavior?
4. Folk tales are brief stories that teach lessons about life. In what ways does "The Old Grandfather and His Little Grandson" fit the definition of a folk tale?

Go Beyond (Apply)

5. What conflicts often occur in relationships between generations, as shown in "The Old Grandfather and His Little Grandson"?

Develop Reading and Literary Skills

Infer Theme From Actions

Folk tales, like other kinds of literature, usually communicate a **theme**—that is, a message or idea about life. Sometimes you need to figure out the theme by making **inferences** about what is going on in the story. You examine the problem that the plot focuses on and notice how characters respond to the problem.

1. What problem does the plot explore?
2. What can you infer about relationships between generations from the characters' behavior in "The Old Grandfather and His Little Grandson"?
3. Basing your inference on your answers to questions 1 and 2, what would you say is the theme of this folk tale?

Ideas for Writing

Stories that pass wisdom from generation to generation are important for the lessons and ideas that they convey.

Firsthand Biography Tell about the life of an elderly person whom you know well. Focus on an incident that influenced the person strongly or that taught an important lesson.

Original Folk Tale Write your own short folk tale focusing on an elderly person. Make sure that the characters and plot of the folk tale teach a lesson about growing older or about relationships between different generations.

Ideas for Projects

Folk-Tale Collection Collect folk tales that convey themes or messages about family relationships, as in "The Old Grandfather and His Little Grandson." Work with a group to comb through anthologies, and select two or three tales that treat similar themes. Group your collected tales by theme and present them to the class.

Wall Collage Create a giant class collage of photographs or other pictures, clippings, and writings about elderly people (grandparents, friends/neighbors, famous people) who have inspired or influenced you. Use the collage as a springboard for sharing stories about these people with the class. [Art Link]

How Am I Doing?

Take a moment to write answers to these questions:

What inferences led me to the theme of this folk tale?

Which piece of my work helped me most to understand family relationships?

Good Hot Dogs *Buenos Hot Dogs* by Sandra Cisneros
For My Sister Molly Who in the Fifties by Alice Walker

What childhood activities do you love and remember best?

Reach Into Your Background

Fond childhood memories may be built on special activities with friends or family members. For example, you may have favorite stories or songs that you enjoyed sharing, or specific games you enjoyed playing together.

- In a small group describe specific songs or games you remember sharing with others when you were younger. Why are they so memorable?
- Give an impromptu "how-to" talk on how to play your favorite game.

Read Actively

Identify Relationships in a Poem

Memories are often the subject of songs and poems. These two poems, "Good Hot Dogs" and "For My Sister Molly . . . ," each describe memories of valuable relationships between the **speaker** (the person who tells the poem) and a special person. To focus on the speakers and the memories they describe, make a two-column chart. As you read, list the different memories that each speaker mentions.

Good Hot Dogs

for Kiki

Sandra Cisneros

Fifty cents apiece
To eat our lunch
We'd run
Straight from school
Instead of home
Two blocks
Then the store
That smelled like steam
You ordered
Because you had the money
Two hot dogs and two pops for here
Everything on the hot dogs
Except pickle lily[1]
Dash those hot dogs
Into buns and splash on
All that good stuff
Yellow mustard and onions
And french fries piled on top all
Rolled up in a piece of wax
Paper for us to hold hot
In our hands
Quarters on the counter
Sit down
Good hot dogs
We'd eat
Fast till there was nothing left
But salt and poppy seeds even
The little burnt tips
Of french fries
We'd eat
You humming
And me swinging my legs

---

1. pickle lily: A slang spelling of "piccalilli,"
a very spicy relish originally coming from the
East Indies.

Buenos Hot Dogs

para Kiki

Translated from the English by the poet

Cincuenta centavos cada uno
Para comer nuestro lonche
Corríamos
Derecho desde la escuela
En vez de a casa
Dos cuadras
Después la tienda
Que olía a vapor
Tú pedías
Porque tenías el dinero
Dos hot dogs y dos refrescos para comer
    aquí
Los hot dogs con todo
Menos pepinos
Hecha esos hot dogs
En sus panes y salpícalos
Con todas esas cosas buenas
Mostaza amarilla y cebollas
Y papas fritas amontonadas encima
Envueltos en papel de cera
Para llevarlos calientitos
En las manos
Monedas encima del mostrador
Siéntate
Buenos hot dogs
Corríamos
Rápido hasta que no quedaba nada
Menos sal y semillas de amapola hasta
Las puntitas quemadas
De las papas fritas
Comíamos
Tú canturreando
Y yo columpiando mis piernas

In an interview, **Sandra Cisneros** (1954–) describes her feelings about writing poetry:

"Poetry is the art of telling the truth. The scariest thing to me is writing poetry, because you're looking at yourself *desnuda*. You're always looking at the part of you that you don't show anybody. The part that your siblings or your parents have never seen. And that center, that terrifying center, is a poem. . . .

"You don't even know what the truth is! You just have to keep writing and hope that you'll come upon something that shocks you. When you think: 'Oh my goodness, I didn't know I felt that!' that's where you stop. That's the little piece of gold you've been looking for. That's a poem."

Respond

The speaker in the poem describes going for hot dogs as a favorite childhood activity. What special activities did you share with friends? Write about one of them in your journal.

For My Sister Molly Who in the Fifties

Alice Walker

Once made a fairy rooster from
Mashed potatoes
Whose eyes I forget
But green onions were his tail
And his two legs were carrot sticks
A tomato slice his crown.[1]
Who came home on vacation
When the sun was hot
and cooked
and cleaned
And minded least of all
The children's questions
A million or more
Pouring in on her
Who had been to school
And knew (and told us too) that certain
Words were no longer good
And taught me not to say us for we
No matter what "Sonny said" up the
road.

FOR MY SISTER MOLLY
WHO IN THE FIFTIES
Knew Hamlet well and read into the night
And coached me in my songs of Africa

---

1. crown (KROWN) *n.*: The red comb on top of the rooster's head.

A continent I never knew
But learned to love
Because "they" she said could carry
A tune
And spoke in accents never heard
In Eatonton.[2]
Who read from *Prose and Poetry*
And loved to read "Sam McGee from Tennessee"
On nights the fire was burning low
And Christmas wrapped in angel hair[3]
And I for one prayed for snow.

WHO IN THE FIFTIES
Knew all the written things that made
Us laugh and stories by
The hour   Waking up the story buds
Like fruit. Who walked among the flowers
And brought them inside the house
And smelled as good as they
And looked as bright.
Who made dresses, braided
Hair. Moved chairs about
Hung things from walls
Ordered baths
Frowned on wasp bites
And seemed to know the endings
Of all the tales
I had forgot.

—————————
2. **Eatonton** (EET in tun): A town in Georgia.
3. **angel hair:** Fine, white, filmy Christmas tree decoration.

 **Respond**

The speaker in the poem has a special relationship to her older sister. What qualities would you value in Molly as a sister?

Then: At the age of eight, **Alice Walker** (1944–   ) was permanently blinded in one eye when her older brother accidentally shot her with a BB gun. Because of the scar tissue that formed on her eye, she felt deformed and ugly and withdrew from people. She began writing poetry to help cure her loneliness. Because of the accident, Walker says she "began to really see people and things, to really notice relationships and to learn to be patient enough to care about how they turned out."

Now: Walker has published several books of poetry as well as novels such as the Pulitzer Prize–winning *The Color Purple*. She explains, "I think my poems today are more about the world outside myself. It is more definitely a poetry of reclaiming ancient, global connections that I wasn't aware of when I was younger. I love writing poetry—it must be the next best thing to singing beautifully."

Explore Your Reading

Look Back (Recall)

1. In "Good Hot Dogs," who always ordered the hot dogs, and why?
2. What did Molly teach the speaker not to say in "For My Sister Molly . . ."?

Think It Over (Interpret)

3. Why does the speaker in "Good Hot Dogs" go into such detail to describe how she bought and ate hot dogs? What sense images stand out for you in that description?
4. Who do you think is the "you" in "Good Hot Dogs"? Explain.
5. The speaker in "For My Sister Molly. . . " tells many things that Molly did, rather than stating her feelings for Molly. How can you tell what her feelings are for Molly?
6. What would you say is the most important thing Molly did for the speaker?

Go Beyond (Apply)

7. Do you think childhood experiences are better in memory than they actually were in real life? Why or why not?

Develop Reading and Literary Skills

Appreciate Lyric Poetry

Poems that express the observations and feelings of a speaker are called **lyric poems.** They are called *lyric* because in ancient times poems like these were sung to the accompaniment of a lyre, a stringed instrument similar to a guitar. In fact, the word *lyrics* today means the words of a song accompanied by music.

You can think of the two lyric poems "Good Hot Dogs" and "For My Sister Molly . . ." as songs that the poets are singing to express feelings about people and times in their lives. Use the memories you listed in your chart to answer these questions.

1. What do these memories tell about the relationships between the people?

2. How are the two relationships similar?
3. In what respect are the poems lyrical?

Ideas for Writing

Celebrating people and our memories of them can take many forms.

Character Description Basing your ideas on "For My Sister Molly . . . ," write a character description of the speaker's sister Molly. Tell how old you think Molly is, how she feels about the speaker, how Molly interacts with other family members, and, most important, what her personality traits are.

Poetic Tribute Write a poem paying tribute to a person from your childhood—a brother, sister, or other relative, or a friend or teacher. Work your poem around a list of things that person did, as in "For My Sister Molly. . . ," or focus on a memorable activity you shared, as in "Good Hot Dogs."

Ideas for Projects

Research With a group, research the 1950's. Make a list of aspects of the 1950's you'd like to know about—the music, TV shows, clothing, current events, art, scientific discoveries, popular fads. Include interviews with people you know who experienced the era firsthand. Report your findings to the class. [Social Studies Link]

Cookbook Create a cookbook of foods you remember and love from your childhood. Include descriptions of times when you used to eat the foods, and, if you can, describe how to prepare them. Compile your recipes with those of other students to create a cookbook. Share your cookbook with the class.

How Am I Doing?

Take a moment to write responses to these questions in your journal:

What aspect of lyric poetry is most clear to me?

Which form was most useful in expressing the relationship I most admire?

Why is it important to have pride in your heritage?

Reach Into Your Background

What kinds of heirlooms, or special keep-sakes, have special meaning for families? One might be a piece of furniture that has been passed down from an earlier generation. Jewelry, photographs, and letters are other items a family might treasure. Can you imagine a situation in which someone might be embarrassed about something from a family's heritage?

In your journal write about a family heirloom, real or imagined. What is its history? What would you tell your friends about it?

Read Actively

Recognize Characters' Motivation

Part of the fun in reading a story is getting to know the people in it and thinking about why they act as they do, just as you would with real-life people. Like real people, characters in stories may have a variety of **motives,** or reasons for doing what they do.

As you read "The Medicine Bag," keep a list of the actions of the two main characters, Martin and Joe Iron Shell. Use a chart like this one to note the specific actions of the characters and the reasons why they do them.

	What he does	Why he does it
Martin	_____	_____
	_____	_____
Joe Iron Shell	_____	_____

The Medicine Bag

Virginia Driving Hawk Sneve

My kid sister Cheryl and I always bragged about our Sioux[1] grandpa, Joe Iron Shell. Our friends, who had always lived in the city and only knew about Indians from movies and TV, were impressed by our stories. Maybe we exaggerated and made Grandpa and the reservation sound glamorous, but when we'd return home to Iowa after our yearly summer visit to Grandpa, we always had some exciting tale to tell.

We always had some authentic Sioux article to show our listeners. One year Cheryl had new moccasins[2] that Grandpa had made. On another visit he gave me a small, round, flat, rawhide drum that was decorated with a painting of a warrior riding a horse. He taught me a real Sioux chant to sing while I beat the drum with a leather-covered stick that had a feather on the end. Man, that really made an impression.

We never showed our friends Grandpa's picture. Not that we were ashamed of him, but because we

> 📖 **Read Actively**
> **Predict** how Martin will relate to his Sioux grandpa.

knew that the glamorous tales we told didn't go with the real thing. Our friends would have laughed at the picture because Grandpa wasn't tall and stately like TV Indians. His hair wasn't in braids but hung in stringy, gray strands on his neck, and he was old. He was our great-grandfather, and he didn't live in a tipi,[3] but all by himself in a part log, part tar-paper shack on the Rosebud Reservation[4] in South Dakota. So when Grandpa came to visit us, I was so ashamed and embarrassed I could've died.

There are a lot of yippy poodles and other fancy little dogs in our neighborhood, but they usually barked singly at the mailman from the safety of their own yards. Now it sounded as if a whole pack of mutts were barking together in one place.

I got up and walked to the curb to see what the commotion was. About a block away I saw a crowd of little kids yelling, with the dogs yipping and growling around someone who was walking down the middle of the street.

I watched the group as it slowly came closer and saw that in the center of the strange procession was a man wearing a tall black hat. He'd pause now and then to peer at something in his hand and then at the houses on either side of the street. I felt cold and hot at the same time as I recognized the man. "Oh, no!" I whispered. "It's Grandpa!"

I stood on the curb, unable to move even though I wanted to run and hide. Then I got mad when I saw how the yippy dogs were growling and nipping at the old man's baggy pant legs and how wearily he poked them

> 📖 **Read Actively**
> **Visualize** how Joe Iron Shell looks as he walks up the street. How does he contrast with the suburban neighborhood?

---

[4]. **Rosebud Reservation:** A small Indian reservation in south-central South Dakota.

---

[1]. **Sioux** (SOO): Native American tribes of the northern plains of the United States and nearby southern Canada.

[2]. **moccasins** (MOK e sinz) *n.*: Heelless slippers of soft flexible leather, originally worn by Native Americans.

[3]. **tipi** (TEE pee) *n.*: A cone-shaped tent of animal skins, used by the Plains Indians.

Words to Know

procession (proh SESH uhn) *n.*: A long line of people walking

away with his cane. "Stupid mutts," I said as I ran to rescue Grandpa.

When I kicked and hollered at the dogs to get away, they put their tails between their legs and scattered. The kids ran to the curb where they watched me and the old man.

"Grandpa," I said and felt pretty dumb when my voice cracked. I reached for his beat-up old tin suitcase, which was tied shut with a rope. But he set it down right in the street and shook my hand.

"*Hau, Takoza*, Grandchild," he greeted me formally in Sioux.

All I could do was stand there with the whole neighborhood watching and shake the hand of the leather-brown old man. I saw how his gray hair straggled from under his big black hat, which had a drooping feather in its crown. His rumpled black suit hung like a sack over his stooped frame. As he shook my hand, his coat fell open to expose a bright red satin shirt with a beaded bolo tie[5] under the collar. His get-up wasn't out of place on the reservation, but it sure was here, and I wanted to sink right through the pavement.

> **📖 Read Actively**
>
> **Ask yourself** why Martin is embarrassed. Is it understandable for him to feel this way?

"Hi," I muttered with my head down. I tried to pull my hand away when I felt his bony hand trembling, and looked up to see fatigue in his face. I felt like crying. I couldn't think of anything to say so I picked up Grandpa's suitcase, took his arm, and guided him up the driveway to our house.

Mom was standing on the steps. I don't know how long she'd been watching, but her hand was over her mouth and she looked as if she couldn't believe what she saw. Then she ran to us.

"Grandpa," she gasped. "How in the world did you get here?"

She checked her move to embrace Grandpa and I remembered that such a display of affection is unseemly to the Sioux and would embarrass him.

"*Hau*, Marie," he said as he shook Mom's hand. She smiled and took his other arm.

As we supported him up the steps, the door banged open and Cheryl came bursting out of the house. She was all smiles and was so obviously glad to see Grandpa that I was ashamed of how I felt.

"Grandpa!" she yelled happily. "You came to see us!"

Grandpa smiled, and Mom and I let go of him as he stretched out his arms to my ten-year-old sister, who was still young enough to be hugged.

"*Wicincala*, little girl," he greeted her and then collapsed.

He had fainted. Mom and I carried him into her sewing room, where we had a spare bed.

After we had Grandpa on the bed Mom stood there helplessly patting his shoulder.

"Shouldn't we call the doctor, Mom?" I suggested, since she didn't seem to know what to do.

"Yes," she agreed with a sigh. "You make Grandpa comfortable, Martin."

I reluctantly moved to the bed. I knew Grandpa wouldn't want to have Mom undress him, but I didn't want to, either. He was so skinny and frail that his coat slipped off easily. When I loosened his tie and opened his shirt collar, I felt a small leather pouch that hung from a thong[6] around his neck. I left it alone and moved to remove his boots. The scuffed old cowboy boots were tight and he moaned as I put pressure on his legs to jerk them off.

I put the boots on the floor and saw why they fit so tight. Each one was stuffed with money. I looked at the bills that lined the boots and started to ask about them, but

> **📖 Read Actively**
>
> **Connect** with Martin's feelings about his grandfather. What motivates him to act as he does?

---

5. **bolo** (BOH loh) **tie** *n.*: A man's string tie, held together with a decorated sliding device.

6. **thong** *n.*: A narrow strip of leather.

Words to Know

fatigue (fuh TEEG) *n.*: Great weariness

Grandpa's eyes were closed again.

Mom came back with a basin of water. "The doctor thinks Grandpa is suffering from heat exhaustion," she explained as she bathed Grandpa's face. Mom gave a big sigh, "*Oh hinh*, Martin. How do you suppose he got here?"

We found out after the doctor's visit. Grandpa was angrily sitting up in bed while Mom tried to feed him some soup.

"Tonight you let Marie feed you, Grandpa," spoke my dad, who had gotten home from work just as the doctor was leaving. "You're not really sick," he said as he gently pushed Grandpa back against the pillows. "The doctor said you just got too tired and hot after your long trip."

Grandpa relaxed, and between sips of soup, he told us of his journey. Soon after our visit to him Grandpa decided that he would like to see where his only living descendants lived and what our home was like. Besides, he admitted sheepishly, he was lonesome after we left.

I knew everybody felt as guilty as I did—especially Mom. Mom was all Grandpa had left. So even after she married my dad, who's a white man and teaches in the college in our city, and after Cheryl and I were born, Mom made sure that every summer we spent a week with Grandpa.

I never thought that Grandpa would be lonely after our visits, and none of us noticed how old and weak he had become. But Grandpa knew and so he came to us. He had ridden on buses for two and a half days. When he arrived in the city, tired and stiff from sitting for so long, he set out, walking, to find us.

Buckskin Shield cover
American Museum of Natural History

He had stopped to rest on the steps of some building downtown, and a policeman found him. The cop, according to Grandpa, was a good man who took him to the bus stop and waited until the bus came and told the driver to let Grandpa out at Bell View Drive. After Grandpa got off the bus, he started walking again. But he couldn't see the house numbers on the other side when he walked on the sidewalk so he walked in the middle of the street. That's when all the little kids and dogs followed him.

I knew everybody felt as bad as I did. Yet I was so proud of this eighty-six-year-old man, who had never been away from the reservation, having the courage to travel so far alone.

"You found the money in my boots?" he asked Mom.

"Martin did," she answered, and roused herself to scold. "Grandpa, you shouldn't have carried so much money. What if someone had stolen it from you?"

Grandpa laughed. "I would've known if anyone tried to take the boots off my feet. The money is what I've saved for a long time—a hundred dollars—for my funeral. But you take it now to buy groceries so that I won't be a burden to you while I am here."

"That won't be necessary, Grandpa," Dad said. "We are honored to have you with us, and you will never be a burden. I am only sorry that we never thought to bring you home with us this summer and spare you the discomfort of a long trip."

Grandpa was pleased. "Thank you," he answered. "But do not feel bad that you didn't bring me with you for I would not have come then. It was not time." He said this in such a

Indian on a Galloping Horse after Remington No. 2, 1976 Fritz Scholder
Collection of the Museum of Fine Arts
Museum of New Mexico

way that no one could argue with him. To Grandpa and the Sioux, he once told me, a thing would be done when it was the right time to do it, and that's the way it was.

"Also," Grandpa went on, looking at me, "I have come because it is soon time for Martin to have the medicine bag."

We all knew what that meant. Grandpa thought he was going to die, and he had to follow the tradition of his family to pass the medicine bag, along with its history, to the oldest male child.

"Even though the boy," he said still looking at me, "bears a white man's name, the medicine bag will be his."

I didn't know what to say. I had the same hot and cold feeling that I had when I first saw Grandpa in the street. The medicine bag was the dirty leather pouch I had found around his neck. "I could never wear such a thing," I almost said aloud. I thought of having my friends see it in gym class or at the swimming pool and could imagine the smart things they would say. But I just swallowed hard and took a step toward the bed. I knew I would have to take it.

But Grandpa was tired. "Not now, Martin," he said, waving his hand in dismissal. "It is not time. Now I will sleep."

So that's how Grandpa came to be with us for two months. My friends kept asking to come see the old man, but I put them off. I told myself that I didn't want them laughing at Grandpa.

But even as I made excuses, I knew it wasn't Grandpa that I was afraid they'd laugh at.

Nothing bothered Cheryl about bringing her friends to see Grandpa. Every day after school started, there'd be a crew of giggling little girls or round-eyed little boys crowded around the old man on the patio, where he'd gotten in the habit of sitting every afternoon.

Grandpa would smile in his gentle way and patiently answer their questions, or he'd tell them stories of brave warriors, ghosts, animals, and the kids listened in awed silence. Those little guys thought Grandpa was great.

Finally, one day after school, my friends came home with me because nothing I said stopped them. "We're going to see the great Indian of Bell View Drive," said Hank, who was supposed to be my best friend. "My brother has seen him three times so he oughta be well enough to see us."

When we got to my house, Grandpa was sitting on the patio. He had on his red shirt, but today he also wore a fringed leather vest that was decorated with beads. Instead of his usual cowboy boots, he had solidly beaded moccasins on his feet that stuck out of his black trousers. Of course, he had his old black hat on—he was seldom without it. But it had been brushed, and the feather in the beaded headband was proudly erect, its tip a brighter white. His hair lay in silver strands over the red shirt collar.

I stared just as my friends did, and I heard one of them murmur, "Wow!"

Grandpa looked up and when his eyes met mine they twinkled as if he were laughing inside. He nodded to me and my face got all hot. I could tell that he had known all along I was afraid he'd embarrass me in front of my friends.

"*Hau, hoksilas,* boys," he greeted and held out his hand.

My buddies passed in a single file and shook his hand as I introduced them. They were so polite I almost laughed. "How, there, Grandpa," and even a "How-do-you-do, sir."

"You look fine, Grandpa," I said as the guys sat on the lawn chairs or on the patio floor.

"*Hanh,* yes," he agreed. "When I woke up

this morning, it seemed the right time to dress in the good clothes. I knew that my grandson would be bringing his friends."

"You guys want some lemonade or something?" I offered. No one answered. They were listening to Grandpa as he started telling how he'd killed the deer from which his vest was made.

Grandpa did most of the talking while my friends were there. I was so proud of him and amazed at how respectfully quiet my buddies were. Mom had to chase them home at supper time. As they left, they shook Grandpa's hand again and said to me:

"Martin, he's really great!"

"Yeah, man! Don't blame you for keeping him to yourself."

"Can we come back?"

But after they left, Mom said, "No more visitors for a while, Martin. Grandpa won't admit it, but his strength hasn't returned. He likes having company, but it tires him."

That evening Grandpa called me to his room before he went to sleep. "Tomorrow," he said, "when you come home, it will be time to give you the medicine bag."

I felt a hard squeeze from where my heart is supposed to be and was scared, but I answered, "OK, Grandpa."

All night I had weird dreams about thunder and lightning on a high hill. From a distance I heard the slow beat of a drum. When I woke up in the morning, I felt as if I hadn't slept at all. At school it seemed as if the day would never end and, when it finally did, I ran home.

Grandpa was in his room, sitting on the bed. The shades were down, and the place was dim and cool. I sat on the floor in front of Grandpa, but he didn't even look at me. After

what seemed a long time he spoke.

"I sent your mother and sister away. What you will hear today is only for a man's ears. What you will receive is only for a man's hands." He fell silent and I felt shivers down my back.

"My father in his early manhood," Grandpa began, "made a vision quest[7] to find a spirit guide for his life. You cannot understand how it was in that time, when the great Teton Sioux were first made to stay on the reservation. There was a strong need for guidance from *Wakantanka*,[8] the Great Spirit. But too many of the young men were filled with despair and hatred. They thought it was hopeless to search for a vision when the glorious life was gone and only the hated confines of a reservation lay ahead. But my father held to the old ways.

"He carefully prepared for his quest with a purifying sweat bath and then he went alone to a high butte top to fast and pray. After three days he received his sacred dream—in which he found, after long searching, the white man's iron. He did not understand his vision of finding something belonging to the white people, for in that time they were the enemy. When he came down from the butte to cleanse himself at the stream below, he found the remains of a campfire and the broken shell of an iron kettle. This was a sign that reinforced his dream. He took a piece of the iron for his medicine bag, which he had made of elk skin years before, to prepare for his quest.

"He returned to his village, where he told his dream to the wise old men of the tribe. They gave him the name *Iron Shell*, but neither did they understand the meaning of the dream. This first Iron Shell kept the piece of iron with him at all times and believed it gave him protection from the evils of those unhappy days.

"Then a terrible thing happened to Iron Shell. He and several other young men were taken from their homes by the soldiers and sent

---

Words to Know

dismissal (dis MIS uhl) *n.*: Sending someone away
purifying (PYOR uh fī ing) *adj.*: Ridding of polluting matter
butte (BYOOT) *n.*: A steep hill rising up from a flat plain
reinforced (ree in FORST) *v.*: Strengthened

---

7. **vision quest:** A search for a revelation that would aid understanding.
8. **Wakantanka** (wah kin TAHNK uh): The Sioux religion's most important spirit—the creator of the world.

far away to a white man's boarding school. He was angry and lonesome for his parents and the young girl he had wed before he was taken away. At first Iron Shell resisted the teacher's attempts to change him and he did not try to learn. One day it was his turn to work in the school's blacksmith shop. As he walked into the place he knew that his medicine had brought him there to learn and work with the white man's iron.

"Iron Shell became a blacksmith and worked at the trade when he returned to the reservation. All of his life he treasured the medicine bag. When he was old, and I was a man, he gave it to me, for no one made the vision quest any more."

Grandpa quit talking and I stared in disbelief as he covered his face with his hands. His shoulders were shaking with quiet sobs and I looked away until he began to speak again.

"I kept the bag until my son, your mother's father, was a man and had to leave us to fight in the war across the ocean. I gave him the bag, for I believed it would protect him in battle, but he did not take it with him. He was afraid that he would lose it. He died in a faraway place."

Again Grandpa was still and I felt his grief around me.

"My son," he went on after clearing his throat, "had only a daughter and it is not proper for her to know of these things."

He unbuttoned his shirt, pulled out the leather pouch, and lifted it over his head. He held it in his hand, turning it over and over as if memorizing how it looked.

"In the bag," he said as he opened it and removed two objects, "is the broken shell of the iron kettle, a pebble from the butte, and a piece of the sacred sage."[9] He held the pouch upside down and dust drifted down.

"After the bag is yours you must put a piece of prairie sage within and never open it again until you pass it on to your son." He replaced the pebble and the piece of iron, and tied the bag.

---

9. **sage** (SAYJ) *n*.: A grayish-green herb of the mint family, sometimes believed to have healing powers.

I stood up, somehow knowing I should. Grandpa slowly rose from the bed and stood upright in front of me holding the bag before my face. I closed my eyes and waited for him to slip it over my head. But he spoke.

"No, you need not wear it." He placed the soft leather bag in my right hand and closed my other hand over it. "It would not be right to wear it in this time and place where no one will understand. Put it safely away until you are again on the reservation. Wear it then, when you replace the sacred sage."

Grandpa turned and sat again on the bed. Wearily he leaned his head against the pillow. "Go," he said. "I will sleep now."

"Thank you, Grandpa," I said softly and left with the bag in my hands.

That night Mom and Dad took Grandpa to the hospital. Two weeks later I stood alone on the lonely prairie of the reservation and put the sacred sage in my medicine bag.

Respond

- How do you think Martin felt standing on the prairie at the end of the story?
- Sketch a picture of Martin putting the sage in his medicine bag.

Virginia Driving Hawk Sneve (1933–) is a member of the Rosebud Sioux tribe of Native Americans and grew up on the Rosebud Reservation in South Dakota. In an interview Sneve said, "In my writing, I try to present an accurate portrayal of American Indian life as I have known it. I also attempt to interpret history from the viewpoint of the American Indian."

"In doing so," she says in another statement, "I hope to dispel stereotypes and to show my reading audience that Native Americans have a proud past, a viable present, and a hopeful future."

Explore Your Reading

Look Back (Recall)

1. What is the medicine bag, and what does it contain?

Think It Over (Interpret)

2. How do Martin's feelings about his grandfather change during the story, and why?
3. Why is the medicine bag important to the old man?
4. The grandfather's father went on a vision quest as part of Sioux tradition. In what sense does Martin also go on a vision quest, and what does he learn?

Go Beyond (Apply)

5. What might Americans from different cultural backgrounds do to get in touch with their heritages?

Develop Reading and Literary Skills

Understand Characters' Motivation

Once you have identified the actions of characters, you can look behind them to understand the characters' **motives,** the reasons that they behave as they do. For example, you can see that Joe Iron Shell's reason for making the journey to his family is to give Martin the medicine bag.

Identify the characters' motivation at the end of the story. Use information from your chart to answer these questions:

1. Why does Joe Iron Shell give the medicine bag to Martin?
2. Why does Martin accept the medicine bag?

Ideas for Writing

Martin's grandfather leaves a memorable legacy to his grandson. Explore different ways in which traditions are passed on.

Research Report Do research and write a report on a cultural tradition or custom that you know or have heard about—for example, lighting a candle or tying a ribbon around a tree to remember someone. What is the meaning of the custom? What is its history? Has it changed over time and, if so, how?

Letter From a Character Write a letter from Joe Iron Shell to Martin, explaining why he gave Martin the medicine bag. The letter should try to persuade Martin to continue the Sioux tradition of the medicine bag. Make your letter sound the way the old man speaks.

Letter to the Future Write a letter that Martin might write to his son in the future, as he passes on the medicine bag. The letter should explain the Sioux tradition and Martin's personal reflections on receiving and passing on the medicine bag.

Ideas for Projects

Research Presentation Research the traditions of a Native American group that lived near your community. Collect photographs, pictures, and objects, and gather stories and information about the group's daily lives. Present this material to the class in a dramatization, a piece of art, an oral report, or a documentary videotape.

Taped Interview Interview a grandparent or an elderly friend about an important tradition or custom in his or her background. Prepare a list of questions beforehand, and ask follow-up questions. Record the interview on audiotape. Edit your interview and play it for the class.

How Am I Doing?

Respond briefly to these questions:

What have I learned about analyzing motivation in a fictional character?

Which piece of my work best shows my understanding of this story?

How does it feel to go to a new school for the first time?

Reach Into Your Background

When people move to a new school or a new neighborhood, they meet many people for the first time. How do they get to know people in the neighborhood? In your school, how do new students meet people? Do they just bravely walk up to you and introduce themselves?

- In a small group, share your experiences meeting someone new. Identify strategies that could be successful in making friends.
- Jot in your journal the feelings you remember when meeting new people.

Read Actively

Examine Character Behavior

The characters in "The Osage Orange Tree," high school students during the Depression of the 1930's, become friends in an unusual way. Both their own personalities and the difficult financial circumstances of the Depression contribute to their strange friendship.

Like any people you meet, you learn about these characters **indirectly**—from what they do and say, and perhaps from what they *don't* do. As you read, list in your journal your impressions of the two characters—the narrator and Evangeline. Next to each impression you write, tell what the character says or does—or doesn't do—that gives you that impression. Use a chart like this one to record your observations about each character.

Impression	Character's actions	Things *not* done

The Osage Orange Tree

William Stafford

On that first day of high school in the prairie town where the tree was, I stood in the sun by the flagpole and watched, but pretended not to watch, the others. They stood in groups and talked and knew each other, all except one— a girl though—in a faded blue dress, carrying a sack lunch and standing near the corner looking everywhere but at the crowd.

I might talk to her, I thought. But of course it was out of the question.

That first day was easier when the classes started. Some of the teachers were kind; some were frightening. Some of the students didn't care, but I listened and waited; and at the end of the day I was relieved, less conspicuous from then on.

But that day was not really over. As I hurried to carry my new paper route, I was thinking about how in a strange town, if you are quiet, no one notices, and some may like you, later. I was thinking about this when I reached the north edge of town where the scattering houses dwindle. Beyond them to the north lay just openness, the plains, a big swoop of nothing. There, at the last house, just as I cut across a lot and threw to the last customer, I saw the girl in the blue dress coming along the street, heading on out of town, carrying books. And she saw me.

Arnold Comes of Age (detail), 1930 Grant Wood, Sheldon Memorial Art Gallery, University of Nebraska–Lincoln, © 1996 Estate of Grant Wood/ Licensed by VAGA, New York, New York

"Hello."

"Hello."

And because we stopped we were friends. I didn't know how I could stop, but I didn't hurry on. There was nothing to do but to act as if I were walking on out too. I had three papers left in the bag, and I frantically began to fold them—box them, as we called it—for throwing. We had begun to walk and talk. The girl was timid; I became more bold. Not much, but a little.

"Have you gone to school here before?" I asked.

"Yes, I went here last year."

A long pause. A meadowlark sitting on a fencepost hunched his wings and flew. I kicked through the dust of the road.

I began to look ahead. Where could we possibly be walking to? I couldn't be walking just because I wanted to be with her.

Fortunately, there was one more house, a gray house by a sagging barn, set two hundred yards from the road.

"I thought I'd see if I could get a customer here," I said, waving toward the house.

"That's where I live."

"Oh."

We were at the dusty car tracks that turned off the road to the house. The girl stopped. There was a tree at that corner, a

Words to Know

conspicuous (kuhn SPIK yoo uhs) *adj.*: Easy to notice

dwindle (DWIN duhl) *v.*: Lessen

straight but little tree with slim branches and shiny dark leaves.

"I could take a paper tonight to see if my father wants to buy it."

A great relief, this. What could I have said to her parents? I held out a paper, dropped it, picked it up, brushing off the dust. "No, here's a new one"—a great action, putting the dusty paper in the bag over my shoulder and pulling out a fresh one. When she took the paper we stood there a minute. The wind was coming in over the grass. She looked out with a tranquil expression.

She walked away past the tree, and I hurried quickly back toward town. Could anyone in the houses have been watching? I looked back once. The girl was standing on the small bridge halfway into her house. I hurried on.

The next day at school I didn't ask her whether her father wanted to take the paper.

Ice Glare, 1933
Charles Burchfield, Whitney Museum of American Art

When the others were there I wouldn't say anything. I stood with the boys. In American history the students could choose their seats, and I saw that she was too quiet and plainly dressed for many to notice her. But I crowded in with the boys, pushing one aside, scrambling for a seat by the window.

That night I came to the edge of town. Two papers were left, and I walked on out. The meadowlark was there. By some reeds in a ditch by the road a dragonfly—snake feeders, we called them—glinted. The sun was going down, and the plains were stretched out and lifted, some way, to the horizon. Could I go on up to the house? I didn't

think so, but I walked on. Then, by the tree where her road turned off, she was standing. She was holding her books. More confused than ever, I stopped.

"My father will take the paper," she said.

She told me always to leave the paper at the foot of the tree. She insisted on that, saying their house was too far; and it is true that I was far off my route, a long way, a half-mile out of my territory. But I didn't think of that.

And so we were acquainted. What I remember best in that town was those evening walks to the tree. Every night—or almost every night—the girl was there. Evangeline was her name. We didn't say much. On Friday night of the first week she gave me a dime, the cost of the paper. It was a poor newspaper, by the way, cheap, sensational, unreliable. I never went up to her house. We never talked together at school. But all the time we knew each other; we just happened to meet. Every evening.

There was a low place in the meadow by that corner. The fall rains made a pond there, and in the evening sometimes ducks would be coming in—a long line with set wings down the wind, and then a turn, and a skimming glide to the water. The wind would be blowing and the grass bent down. The evenings got colder and colder. The wind was cold. As winter came on the time at the tree was dimmer, but not dark. In the winter there was snow. The pond was frozen over; all the plains were white. I had to walk down the ruts of the road and leave the paper in the crotch of the tree, sometimes, when it was cold.

Words to Know

tranquil (TRAN kwil) *adj.*: Calm; peaceful
glinted (GLINT ed) *v.*: Flashed

The wind made a sound through the black branches. But usually, even on cold evenings, Evangeline was there.

At school we played ball at noon—the boys did. And I got acquainted. I learned that Evangeline's brother was janitor at the school. A big dark boy he was—a man, middle-aged I thought at the time. He didn't ever let on that he knew me. I would see him sweeping the halls, bent down, slow. I would see him and Evangeline take their sack lunches over to the south side of the building. Once I slipped away from the ball game and went over there, but he looked at me so steadily, without moving, that I pretended to be looking for a book, and quickly went back, and got in the game and struck out.

You don't know about those winters, and especially that winter. Those were the dust years. Wheat was away down in price. Everyone was poor—poor in a way that you can't understand. I made two dollars a week, or something like that, on my paper route. I could tell about working for ten cents an hour—and then not getting paid; about families that ate wheat, boiled, for their main food, and burned wheat for fuel. You don't know how it would be. All through that hard winter I carried a paper to the tree by the pond, in the evening, and gave it to Evangeline.

In the cold weather Evangeline wore a heavier dress, a dark, straight, heavy dress, under a thick black coat. Outdoors she wore a knitted cap that fastened under her chin. She was dressed this way when we met and she took the paper. The reeds were broken now. The meadowlark was gone.

And then came the spring. I have forgotten to tell just how Evangeline looked. She was of medium height, and slim. Her face was pale, her forehead high, her eyes blue. Her tranquil face I remember well. I remember her watching the wind come in over the grass. Her dress was long, her feet small. I can remember her

by the tree, with her books, or walking on up the road toward her house and stopping on the bridge halfway up there, but she didn't wave, and I couldn't tell whether she was watching me or not. I always looked back as I went over the rise toward town.

And I can remember her in the room at school. She came into American history one spring day, the first really warm day. She had changed from the dark heavy dress to the dull

House and Barn in Snow
Jim Harrison, Jim Harrison Gallery

blue one of the last fall; and she had on a new belt, a gray belt, with blue stitchIng along the edges. As she passed in front of Jane Wright, a girl who sat on the front row, I heard Jane say to the girl beside her, "Why look at Evangeline— that old dress of hers has a new belt!"

"Stop a minute, Evangeline," Jane said; "let me see your new dress."

Evangeline stopped and looked uncertainly at Jane and blushed. "It's just made over," she said, "it's just. . . ."

"It's cute, Dear," Jane said; and as Evangeline went on Jane nudged her friend in the ribs and the friend smothered a giggle.

Well, that was a good year. Commencement time came, and—along with the newspaper job—I had the task of preparing for finals and all. One thing, I wasn't a student who took part in the class play or anything like that. I was just one of the boys—twenty-fourth in line to get my diploma.

And graduation was bringing an end to my paper-carrying. My father covered a big territory in our part of the state, selling farm equipment; and we were going to move at once to a town seventy miles south. Only because of my finishing the school year had we stayed till graduation.

I had taught another boy my route, always leaving him at the end and walking on out, by myself, to the tree. I didn't really have to go around with him that last day, the day of graduation, but I was going anyway.

At the graduation exercises, held that May afternoon, I wore my brown Sunday suit. My mother was in the audience. It was a heavy day. The girls had on new dresses. But I didn't see her.

I suppose that I did deserve old man Sutton's "Shhh!" as we lined up to march across the stage, but I for the first time in the year forgot my caution, and asked Jane where Evangeline was. She shrugged, and I could see for myself that she was not there.

We marched across the stage; our diplomas were ours; our parents filed out; to the strains of a march on the school organ we trailed to the hall. I unbuttoned my brown suit coat, stuffed the diploma in my pocket, and sidled out of the group and upstairs.

Evangeline's brother was emptying wastebaskets at the far end of the hall. I sauntered toward him and stopped. I didn't know what I wanted to say. Unexpectedly, he solved my prob-lem. Stopping in his work, holding a partly empty wastebasket over the canvas sack he wore over his shoulder, he stared at me, as if almost to say something.

The Hupper Farm (Evening), 1939
N. C. Wyeth, Dallas Museum of Art

"I noticed that your sister wasn't here," I said. The noise below was dwindling. The hall was quiet, an echoey place; my voice sounded terribly loud. He emptied the rest of the wastebasket and shifted easily. He was a man, in big overalls. He stared at me.

"Evangeline couldn't come," he said. He stopped, looked at me again, and said, "She stole."

"Stole?" I said. "Stole what?"

He shrugged and went toward the next wastebasket, but I followed him.

"She stole the money from her bank—the money she was to use for her graduation dress," he said. He walked stolidly on, and I stopped. He deliberately turned away as he picked up the next wastebasket. But he said something else, half to himself. "You knew her. You talked to her . . . I know." He walked away.

Words to Know

strains (STRAYNZ) *n.*: Bits of music
sauntered (SAWN terd) *v.*: Walked slowly
stolidly (STAHL id lee) *adv.*: Unemotionally
gaunt (GAWNT) *adj.*: Extremely thin
defiant (di FĪ uhnt) *adj.*: Openly rebellious
skulked (SKUHLKT) *v.*: Sneaked

I hurried downstairs and outside. The new carrier would have the papers almost delivered by now; so I ran up the street toward the north. I took a paper from him at the end of the street and told him to go back. I didn't pay any more attention to him.

No one was at the tree, and I turned, for the first time, up the road to the house. I walked over the bridge and on up the narrow, rutty tracks. The house was gray and lopsided. The ground of the yard was packed; nothing grew there. By the back door, the door to which the road led, there was a grayish-white place on the ground where the dishwater had been thrown. A gaunt shepherd dog trotted out growling.

And the door opened suddenly, as if someone had been watching me come up the track. A woman came out—a woman stern-faced, with a shawl over her head and a dark lumpy dress on—came out on the back porch and shouted, "Go 'way, go 'way! We don't want no papers!" She waved violently with one hand, holding the other on her shawl, at her throat. She coughed so hard that she leaned over and put her hand against one of the uprights of the porch. Her face was red. She glanced toward the barn and leaned toward me. "Go 'way!"

Behind me a meadowlark sang. Over all the plains swooped the sky. The land was drawn up somehow toward the horizon.

I stood there, half-defiant, half-ashamed. The dog continued to growl and to pace around me, stiff-legged, his tail down. The windows of the house were all blank, with blinds drawn. I couldn't say anything.

I stood a long time and then, lowering the newspaper I had held out, I stood longer, waiting, without thinking of what to do. The meadowlark bubbled over again, but I turned and walked away, looking back once or twice. The old woman continued to stand, leaning forward, her head out. She glanced at the barn, but didn't call out any more.

My heels dug into the grayish place where the dishwater had been thrown; the dog skulked along behind.

At the bridge, halfway to the road, I stopped and looked back. The dog was lying down again; the porch was empty; and the door was closed. Turning the other way, I looked toward town. Near me stood our ragged little tree—an Osage orange tree it was. It was feebly coming into leaf, green all over the branches, among the sharp thorns. I hadn't wondered before how it grew there, all alone, in the plains country, neglected. Over our pond some ducks came slicing in.

Standing there on the bridge, still holding the folded-boxed-newspaper, that worthless paper, I could see everything. I looked out along the road to town. From the bridge you would see the road going away, to where it went over the rise.

Glancing around, I flipped that last newspaper under the bridge and then bent far over and looked where it had gone. There they were—a pile of boxed newspapers, thrown in a heap, some new, some worn and weathered, by rain, by snow.

Respond

Would you have done what Evangeline did to maintain a friendship? Why or why not?

William Stafford (1914–1993) wrote poetry as well as stories. These are some of his observations on the process of writing.

- "A writer is not so much someone who has something to say as he is someone who has found a process that will bring about new things he would not have thought of if he had not started to say them."
- "I feel very exploratory when I write. . . . I feel like Daniel Boone going into Kentucky. The thing is being there and finding it."
- "Writing [is] in its language aspects a series of moves like dancing."
- Writing "is like fishing. . . . I am headlong to discover."
- "Your job [as a writer] is to find out what the world is trying to be."

Activities
MAKE MEANING

Explore Your Reading

Look Back (Recall)

1. Under what circumstances do the narrator and Evangeline meet each day?
2. According to her brother, why doesn't Evangeline go to the commencement ceremony?

Think It Over (Interpret)

3. Why does Evangeline say her father will take the paper? How does she pay for it?
4. The narrator says that, of everything that happened that year, he chiefly remembers his meetings with Evangeline. Why would this be so?
5. In what ways is Evangeline like the Osage orange tree on her family's farm?

Go Beyond (Apply)

6. What do you think will happen to the Evangeline of this story? Why?

Develop Reading and Literary Skills

Analyze Indirect Characterization

Characters in stories reveal themselves **indirectly** through their actions. Evangeline's actions throughout the story reveal much about her, but it's only at the end of the story, when the narrator reveals the final details, that we really gain insight into her character.

Analyze Evangeline's character using information from your "Read Actively" chart. Answer the following questions:

1. What does her taking the newspaper subscription tell about her?
2. What other clues in the story tell you about her character?
3. Why does she throw the newspapers away?

Ideas for Writing

Stories set in different historical eras help you make connections between the past and the present.

Cause-and-Effect Essay Write an essay analyzing the effects of the Depression era on the characters in "The Osage Orange Tree." Focus particularly on the ending of the story, but include scenes that lead up to it as well.

Letters Connect with the situation of the narrator of "The Osage Orange Tree" when he moves to a new town. Write a letter to Evangeline, expressing your reaction to what she did. You may want to thank her, or tell her that she shouldn't have done it, or offer to keep writing to her. Write an answer from Evangeline.

Ideas for Projects

Depression Documentary Investigate the Depression era. Focus on how conditions in rural areas like that of "The Osage Orange Tree" compared to those of people in urban centers of the country. Collect photographs and art of the era to illustrate the information you find. Include interviews of people who experienced the Depression firsthand. Videotape your documentary, if possible. [Social Studies Link]

Research Graph If you calculate the cost of Evangeline's newspaper for forty weeks, you can estimate that her dress money was about $4.00. Research other prices in this era and compare them to prices today. Prepare a bar graph to show the comparative prices of items in the 1930's and today. [Math Link]

How Am I Doing?

Write a response to one or both of the following questions:

How did reading this story affect the way I view people I have just met?

Which activity helped me to understand how I analyze characters in a story?

How Do I Relate to Others?

Think Critically About the Selections

The selections you have read in this section explore the question "How do I relate to others?" With a partner or a small group, complete one of the following activities to show your understanding of the question. You can present your responses orally or in writing.

1. Most of the selections explore a close relationship between two people. Choose two selections and compare and contrast the relationships they portray. For example, several selections show relationships between family members: grandfathers, sisters, parent and child. One portrays a relationship between a young man and a young woman. **(Compare and Contrast)**

2. The art that appears on this page suggests an answer to the question "How do I relate to others?" Use details of the photograph to write a story about the relationship suggested by the two characters in the art.

3. Some of the selections show characters or speakers making special connections with music, language, or nature. Choose one of the selections that shows such a relationship, and describe the feelings of the central character. Use examples from the selection to back up your ideas. **(Draw Conclusions; Provide Evidence)**

4. Of all the selections, which one portrays a relationship that you would like to see in your own life? What makes this relationship so special to you? **(Synthesize; Draw Conclusions)**

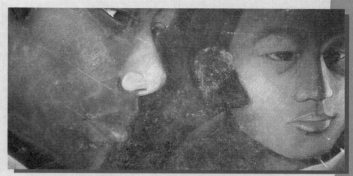

Student Art *Me, Twice Lit in the Shadows* Neng Her Kosciuszko Middle School, Milwaukee, Wisconsin

Projects

Portrait of a Life Identify a person who has been a positive influence or role model for you. Profile this person in both words and pictures, and create a book or a videotape about his or her life. Include quotations from interviews, photographs, drawings, news clippings, and excerpts from correspondence, if available. Present your portrait to the person with your appreciation for what he or she has done for you.

Collage of Influences Create a collage of personal influences for yourself. Begin with a drawing or photograph of yourself, and add pictures or photographs of the people, places, events, and objects that have been important in your life. Plan to combine your collage with those of your classmates to create a wall collage. [Art Link]

Looking at Forms:

Joseph Bruchac

Terms to know

Mood is the feeling or atmosphere created by a literary work.

A **simile** is a figure of speech that makes a direct comparison between two unlike subjects using *like* or *as*.

A **metaphor** is a figure of speech in which something is described as though it were something else. Like a simile, a metaphor works by pointing out a similarity between two unlike things.

When we read a poem, we are not just reading words. In a way, we are reading the mind of the poet who wrote that poem. We are given a glimpse into the ideas and feelings of a distinct individual expressing his or her feelings in a memorable way.

Figurative Language One of the ways in which poetry expresses these ideas and feelings is through the imaginative use of comparisons that we call figurative language. Comparisons using simile and

metaphor assist us in seeing what the poet sees. In a simile, something is described as being *like* something else. In a metaphor, something is described in terms of something else. Both similes and metaphors bring two different things together to create a new idea. When similes and metaphors work well, they help us see and even feel things in ways that are new but seem familiar.

Camille Andrews's "Lanterns" is a memory poem about catching fireflies. It is something many children have done, yet few describe it as well as she does in her poem. One of her metaphors is of the child "cat-pausing in blue twilight." Notice how the comparison between a firefly-catcher and a stalking cat helps to deepen the experience of the poem.

In Lillian Morrison's poem "The Possessors," the poet herself is caught by the very words she uses. They possess her! The words, and even the sounds from which words are made, come alive. They possess the poet who is "embraced by them." Consonants "batter and massage" while the vowels "take me swimming." The playfulness of the poem in its inventive use of metaphor tells you how Morrison feels about writing poetry.

Mood in Poetry Poems are memorable because of figurative language, but they also express a specific emotion, or mood. The mood of a poem is the feeling the poet

Literary Poetry

wants to express about the subject of the poem. Just as the mood of a person can change—from happy to unhappy, from certain to uncertain—we can also talk about the different moods of poems.

Pat Mora's "Maestro" and N. Scott Momaday's "The Delight Song of Tsoai-Talee" are very different in mood. Mora's poem is about a man remembering the sound of his mother's singing voice as he performs music years later. Momaday's poem is a song about his life: Tsoai-Talee is the poet's Kiowan name—which means "Rock-Tree Boy." His poem uses the bright imagery and repetitive structure of the traditional chants of his Native American ancestors.The two very different situations and ideas in these poems produce distinctly different moods.

Joseph Bruchac (1942–   )
Young Joseph grew up in the foothills of the New York Andirondacks with his parents and maternal grandfather. He inherited his great gift for storytelling from his grandfather, as well as his Abekani heritage, though this was not spoken about during his childhood.

Bruchac now lives in those same Adirondack foothills with his wife, with whom he co-founded the Greenfield Review Press, a small publishing house that specializes in Native American poetry and fiction. In addition to his busy schedule as an award-winning writer, storyteller, and lecturer, he is an avid gardener and holds a black belt in Pentjak Silat, the martial art of Indonesia.

The Delight Song of Tsoai-Talee
by N. Scott Momaday
Maestro by Pat Mora

How does a poem express a feeling or a mood?

Reach Into Your Background

Everyone experiences different moods—good moods, bad moods, serious moods, playful moods. Mood refers to people's feelings or emotions and also describes the feeling or emotion communicated by a work of art. For example, a painting full of dark shadows may create a gloomy mood, while bright, bouncy music creates an upbeat mood of excitement. In poetry, mood is created through the words the poet chooses and the voice that speaks them.

With a small group, read the phrase "I am alive" in different tones of voice to communicate different moods, such as anxiety, joy, depression, or contentment. Ask your listeners to identify the mood of each reading.

Read Actively

Identify a Mood

The ideas in a poem come through a speaker, the person who is saying the poem's words. The words of the poem create an atmosphere or feeling that is the speaker's emotions, or mood.

As you read these two poems, list the words or phrases in each poem that create an especially strong mood. Use a chart like this one for each poem, adding lines as needed.

Words and phrases   **Mood**

Words and phrases   **Mood**

Then: When he was an infant, **N. Scott Momaday** (1934–   ), who is half Kiowa Indian, was given the name Tsoai-Talee, or "Rock-Tree Boy," after a butte in Wyoming that is sacred to the Kiowas. To be named after this mythic rock was a great honor, since among Native Americans a name is more than a label—it is a source of someone's character and course of life.

Now: Today, as a poet and Pulitzer Prize–winning novelist, Momaday has a deep concern for maintaining reverence for the Earth and for the creative power of words. He explains, "I believe that the Indian has an understanding of the physical world and of the Earth as a spiritual entity that is very much his own. . . . The whole world view of the Indian is [based on] the principle of harmony in the universe."

The Delight Song of Tsoai-Talee

N. Scott Momaday

I am a feather on the bright sky
I am the blue horse that runs in the plain
I am the fish that rolls, shining, in the water
I am the shadow that follows a child
5   I am the evening light, the luster of meadows
I am an eagle playing with the wind
I am a cluster of bright beads
I am the farthest star
I am the cold of the dawn
10   I am the roaring of the rain
I am the glitter on the crust of the snow
I am the long track of the moon in a lake
I am a flame of four colors
I am a deer standing away in the dusk
15   I am a field of sumac[1] and the pomme blanche[2]
I am an angle of geese in the winter sky
I am the hunger of a young wolf
I am the whole dream of these things

You see, I am alive, I am alive
20   I stand in good relation to the earth
I stand in good relation to the gods
I stand in good relation to all that is beautiful
I stand in good relation to the daughter of *Tsen-tainte*.
You see, I am alive, I am alive

---

1. sumac (SOO mak) *n.*: A treelike plant with
pointed leaves.
2. pomme blanche (pum BLAHNSH) *n.*: French
for "white apple," the fruit of the breadroot plant in
the western United States.

Respond

- What one word sums up
  the mood of this poem?
- Using colors and
  shapes—but not actual,
  recognizable images—
  sketch the mood created
  by this poem.

Words to Know

luster (LUHS ter) *n.*: Glow (line 5)

Maestro[1]

Pat Mora

He hears her
when he bows.
Rows of hands clap
again and again he bows
5   to stage lights and upturned faces
but he hears only his mother's voice

years ago in their small home
singing Mexican songs
one phrase at a time
10   while his father strummed the guitar
or picked the melody with quick fingertips.
Both cast their music in the air
for him to snare with his strings,
songs of *lunas*[2] and *amor*[3]
15   learned bit by bit.
She'd nod, smile, as his bow slid
note to note, then the trio
        voz, guitarra, violín[4]
would blend again and again
20   to the last pure note
sweet on the tongue.

for Abraham Chávez

___

1. maestro (MĪS troh) *n.*: A master in any
art, especially a great composer, conductor, or teacher of music.
2. lunas (LOO nahs) *n.*: Spanish for
"moons."
3. amor (ah MOHR) *n.*: Spanish for "love."
4. voz, guitarra, violín (VOHZ gee TAR
ruh vee oh LEEN): Spanish for "voice,
guitar, violin."

La Guitare Noire, 1926 Juan Gris, University of Iowa Museum of Art

Respond

Does this poem make you feel happy or
a little sad? Explain.

Then: As a child growing up in El Paso,
Texas, **Pat Mora** (1942–   ) resisted the cus-
toms of her Mexican American heritage, feeling that others thought of Hispanics as somehow inferior. Wanting to look and feel
"American," she spoke Spanish only at home
and tried to ignore her cultural background at school.

Now: As a distinguished poet and educator, Mora has
learned to embrace her Hispanic heritage and share it with others. She says, "I revel in a certain Mexican passion in life." In
contrast to her years growing up, Mora explains, "When I hear
a phrase in Spanish in a restaurant, my head turns quickly. I listen, silently wishing to be part of that other conversation—if
only for a few moments, to feel Spanish in my mouth."

Words to Know

snare (SNAYR) *v.*: Capture (line 14)

Activities

MAKE MEANING

Explore Your Reading

Look Back (Recall)

1. What phrases are repeated in "The Delight Song . . ."?
2. What does the violinist in "Maestro" hear instead of the applause that follows his performance?

Think It Over (Interpret)

3. In "The Delight Song . . ." the word "delight" never actually appears. How does the poet create a mood of delight?
4. In "Maestro" why might the performer feel more strongly about his childhood memory than about his present success?

Go Beyond (Apply)

5. What would be a good occasion for a public reading of "The Delight Song . . ."? Explain.
6. Name a famous person who you think would understand the mood communicated in "Maestro."

Develop Reading and Literary Skills

Analyze Mood in Poetry

You can tell someone's mood from his or her tone of voice—whether it moves up or down, stays at the same level, goes fast or slow. When you read a poem, the words of the poem and the way they appear on the page suggest a voice that you "hear" in your imagination. These words give clues to the mood of the poem. For example, in "The Delight Song . . ." the many short lines tumbling forth, each with its own vivid image, create a mood of dizzy happiness.

Analyze the mood of these poems with the help of the words and phrases that you listed in your chart.

1. Identify the mood of "The Delight Song . . ."
2. Explain what features in the poem create that mood.
3. What is the overall mood in "Maestro"?

4. How is this mood created?
5. Does the mood change from the beginning to the end of the poem? Explain.

Ideas for Writing

Moods are important to understand in relating to other people.

Describe a Mood Write a short essay that describes a person in a specific mood, such as delight, anger, sadness, or playfulness. Include specific situations, conversations, and images (such as body language) that convey that mood.

Mood Poems Write two poems that communicate contrasting moods, such as happiness/sadness or delight/anger. Keep the speaker's voice in each poem consistent with the mood you want to express. Illustrate the poems and share them with the class.

Ideas for Projects

Recordings Commercials use moods to sell a product. Record commercials from television or radio that express moods appropriate to different products. Create a grid that shows the mood tied to specific products. Collaborate with a group to write and perform original commercials for similar products.

Art Appreciation Collect paintings, photographs, or drawings that you feel communicate a strong mood. Ask members of your group to identify the mood and explain how the image creates that mood. Prepare a display of images that convey different moods and share them with the class. [Art Link]

How Am I Doing?

Note in your journal responses to these questions:

What details, words, or expressions help me to identify moods?

Which piece of my work expresses a mood most clearly?

What comparisons help to express ideas and feelings?

Reach Into Your Background

Finish these comparisons in the most interesting way you can: "He moved like _____"; "I was as lonely as _____." In each case, you are creating a figure of speech. The most interesting figures of speech are the ones that make the most surprising comparisons. For example, "He shook like an old pickup truck" is a more striking comparison than "He shook like a leaf." Figures of speech provide you with imaginative ways of expressing yourself.

With a small group, brainstorm to compile a list of comparisons that express a specific idea (such as strength or speed) or feeling (such as anger or happiness). Start with easy comparisons and then invent more imaginative ones. For example, for *slippery* you could start with "slippery as an eel" and then come up with "slippery as a wet dachshund."

Read Actively

Identify Comparisons in Poetry

Poets use comparisons to create fresh ways of viewing the world and to allow readers to connect ideas to familiar experiences. Identifying and thinking about the comparisons poets use make poetry easier to understand and more fun to read.

As you read these poems, look for the comparisons the poet makes. List each image or idea and what it is compared to on a chart like this one.

Image or idea	Compared to

Visa, 1951 Stuart Davis, Museum of Modern Art, New York
© 1996 Estate of Stuart Davis/Licensed by VAGA, New York, New York

The Possessors

LILLIAN MORRISON

In the muscles of words
expanding, contracting,
I practice.
I feel their pulse
5   I am embraced by them.

Tongues in your resonant caves
I move and shake with you
to the batter and massage
of consonants
10 and let the vowels
take me swimming.

I want to flex my x's
tumbling, hum my m's
so tendons tremble and cords agree
15 though I polish, they possess,
these sounds own me.

Words to Know

resonant (RES uh nuhnt) *adj.*: Vibrating with sound (line 6)
batter (BAT er) *n.*: Hitting over and over (line 8)
flex (FLEKS) *v.*: Bend and contract, as with a muscle (line12)
tendons (TEN duhnz) *n.*: Tough body tissues that connect the muscles to the bones (line 14)

Lillian Morrison (1917–   ) is best known for her collections of sports poetry, *The Sidewalk Racer* and *Sprints and Distances: Sports in Poetry and the Poetry in Sport.* She has also compiled books of playground chants, autograph album verses, folk rhymes, and riddles from around the world.

Morrison says: "I love rhythms, the body movement implicit in poetry, explicit in sports. I have always believed that the attempt to achieve excellence in either of these fields is both noble and exciting. And there are emotions connected with sports. . . . One turns naturally to poetry to express these things."

Respond

- Which image expresses most closely your own feeling about words?
- List some other things you might compare to your own words.

anterns

Camille Andrews

I remember catching fireflies
in summer dusks
when the warm air hung
like a second skin.

5   I remember darting about the lawn
with a Mason jar,[1]
cat-pausing in blue twilight,
then waiting for small, penlight flashes,
the brush of their wings against my face:
10 a benediction, a kiss.

I remember skipping toward those flashes,
scooping humid air into the jar;
perhaps a miss,
or
15 a lone firefly,
its brief blink signaling my success,
its flash lighting the jar
and the small circle of my hands:
the flickering of an ancient lamp.

20 Tonight,
I see a glimmer in the darkness
feel the faint brush of an idea
across my mind,
and with a pencil and old
25 envelope, I chase after,
seeking the light
of that firefly lantern.

---

1. Mason (MAY sun) **jar** *n.*: A glass jar with a
wide mouth and screw top, used for canning
and preserving.

Words to Know

dusks (DUHSKS) *n.*: Times
just after sunset before nightfall
(line 2)

Respond

- Which comparison in "Lanterns" says the most to you?
- Draw or sketch this image.

Camille Andrews wrote this poem when she was a student at Monacan High School in Richmond, Virginia. It was published in Longwood College's journal, *Virginia Writing*, in 1993.

MAKE MEANING

Explore Your Reading

Look Back (Recall)

1. In "The Possessors," who or what possesses, and who or what is possessed?
2. In "Lanterns," what does the poet feel the "faint brush of" across her mind? What does she use to chase after it?

Think It Over (Interpret)

3. In what sense can words "possess" you?
4. In what ways is a writer like someone chasing fireflies?

Go Beyond (Apply)

5. Both of these poems have something to say about writing. Which most closely describes your experience of writing? Explain.

Develop Reading and Literary Skills

Understand Simile and Metaphor

Two kinds of comparisons, or figures of speech, are similes and metaphors. A **simile** links two different things using the words *like* or *as*. You can probably think of lots of well-known similes using *like* or *as*—"crazy as a loon," "scared as a rabbit," "snug as a bug in a rug."

A **metaphor** compares one thing to another, without using *like* or *as*. "You are my sunshine" is a metaphor from a popular old song. In "The Possessors," "I want to flex my x's/tumbling," is a metaphor suggesting that using words with *x* sounds is an acrobatic exercise of muscles.

Analyze the use of simile and metaphor in these poems.

1. Identify the simile in "Lanterns." Tell what two things are compared using *like* or *as*. Explain the effect of this comparison.
2. Identify a metaphor in "Lanterns." Tell what two things are compared and explain the effect of making this comparison.

3. Choose a metaphor from "The Possessors." Identify the two things being compared and explain the effect of the comparison.

Ideas for Writing

Figures of speech are common in poetry but they also enliven all types of writing.

Evaluate a Figure of Speech Choose a figure of speech from either poem and use it as a springboard for an essay about the idea or feeling it expresses. Discuss the quality of the comparison and evaluate its effectiveness in expressing the idea or feeling.

Poem Write a poem of your own using a central simile or metaphor—for example, compare your day at school to an amusement park ride. Include at least two figures of speech.

Ideas for Projects

Research Report These two poems use fireflies and muscles as central metaphors. Research either fireflies or muscles. Prepare an oral report that shows how your information adds to your understanding of the metaphors in the poems. [Science Link]

Advertisement Plan an advertisement for a product (real or fictional). Create appropriate similes and metaphors to describe the product and make it appeal to buyers. Add appropriate pictures. Present your advertisement to the class and poll students to see if they were encouraged to buy the product.

How Am I Doing?

Take a moment to respond to the following questions:

How do I recognize similes and metaphors?
What can comparisons add to my own writing or speaking?

How Do I Shape My World?

Student Art *On the Wheel* Stratton Huggins
Montgomery Bell Academy, Nashville, Tennessee

Dear Editor,

Student Writing
from Letter to the Editor

  I love to write. When I write, the whole world around me is shut out. I
don't care what else is happening. I enter a world I
create on the spur of the moment. There is no way to stop me;
I won't come back. I am myself . . . .

         Elizabeth Rachel Drew
         Derwood, Maryland

What's the best way to resolve a conflict with an authority figure?

Reach Into Your Background

Imagine that you are living in the 1850's and are learning to pilot a huge steamboat down the Mississippi River to the Gulf of Mexico. What challenges might you face in trying to keep a steamboat on course? Running aground was one important concern. In fact, Samuel Clemens took his pen name, Mark Twain, from a phrase meaning "two fathoms—twelve feet deep," which pilots used as a measure of the safe depth for navigation.

Use one of these activities to help you understand the time and place of this selection.

- Discuss with a small group: What challenges would you expect to find on the job when learning to pilot a steamboat?
- With a partner, role-play an interview for a job you might find on a riverboat, such as cabin boy, deck sweeper, or apprentice pilot.

Read Actively
Identify Conflict

Challenges can sometimes be perceived as conflicts. Most narration—whether fiction or non-fiction—turns on a **conflict,** a problem of some kind. This conflict can be **external**—a problem between two people (*Who will win the argument?*) or between someone and a situation (*Will the boat clear the shallows?*)—or **internal**—within a person (*Should I speak out or keep quiet?*). Finding out how the problem will be taken care of—how the conflict will be resolved—is what keeps us reading a narrative.

As you read Mark Twain's account of his experiences as a young cub pilot on the Mississippi, list the conflicts he meets on the job and the measures he takes to resolve them.

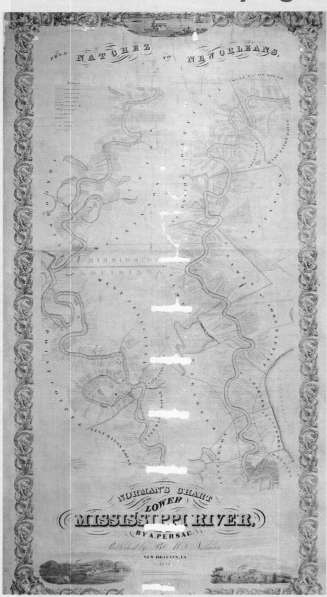

Plantations on the Mississippi River — from Natchez to New Orleans 1858 (Norman Chart)
Historic New Orleans Collection

CUB PILOT ON THE MISSISSIPPI

MARK TWAIN

During the two or two and a half years of my apprenticeship[1] I served under many pilots, and had experience of many kinds of steamboatmen and many varieties of steamboats. I am to this day profiting somewhat by that experience; for in that brief, sharp schooling, I got personally and familiarly acquainted with about all the different types of human nature that are to be found in fiction, biography, or history.

---

1. apprenticeship (a PREN tis ship) *n.*: The time spent by a person working for a master craftsman in a craft or trade in return for instruction and, formerly, support.

The fact is daily borne in upon me that the average shore-employment requires as much as forty years to equip a man with this sort of an education. When I say I am still profiting by this thing, I do not mean that it has constituted me a judge of men—no, it has not done that, for judges of men are born, not made. My profit is various in kind and degree, but the feature of it which I value most is the zest which that early experience has given to my later reading. When I find a well-drawn character in fiction or biography I generally take a warm personal interest in him, for the reason that I have known him before—met him on the river.

The figure that comes before me oftenest, out of the shadows of that vanished time, is that of Brown, of the steamer *Pennsylvania*. He was a middle-aged, long, slim, bony, smooth-shaven, horse-faced, ignorant, stingy, malicious, snarling, fault-hunting, mote[2]-magnifying

___
2. **mote** (MOHT) *n.*: A speck of dust or other tiny particle.

tyrant. I early got the habit of coming on watch with dread at my heart. No matter how good a time I might have been having with the off-watch below, and no matter how high my spirits might be when I started aloft, my soul became lead in my body the moment I approached the pilothouse.

📖 **Read Actively**

Predict the conflict young Mark Twain will describe in this narrative.

I still remember the first time I ever entered the presence of that man. The boat had backed out from St. Louis and was "straightening down." I ascended to the pilothouse in high feather, and very proud to be semiofficially a member of the executive family of so fast and famous a boat. Brown was at the wheel. I paused in the middle of the room, all fixed to make my bow, but Brown did not look around. I thought he took a furtive glance at me out of the corner of his eye, but as not even this notice was repeated, I judged I had been

mistaken. By this time he was picking his way among some dangerous "breaks" abreast the woodyards; therefore it would not be proper to interrupt him; so I stepped softly to the high bench and took a seat.

There was silence for ten minutes; then my new boss turned and inspected me deliberately and painstakingly from head to heel for about—as it seemed to me—a quarter of an hour. After which he removed his countenance[3] and I saw it no more for some seconds; then it came around once more, and this question greeted me: "Are you Horace Bigsby's cub?"[4]

"Yes, sir."

After this there was a pause and another inspection. Then: "What's your name?"

I told him. He repeated it after me. It was probably the only thing he ever forgot; for although I was with him many months he never addressed himself to me in any other way than "Here!" and then his command followed.

"Where was you born?"

"In Florida, Missouri."

A pause. Then: "Dern sight better stayed there!"

By means of a dozen or so of pretty direct questions, he pumped my family history out of me.

The leads[5] were going now in the first crossing. This interrupted the inquest.[6] When the leads had been laid in he resumed:

---

3. **countenance** (KOWN tuh nuhns) *n.*: Face.

4. **cub** (KUHB) *n.*: Beginner.

5. **leads** (LEDZ) *n.*: Weights that were lowered to test the depth of the river.

6. **inquest** (IN kwest) *n.*: Investigation.

"How long you been on the river?"

I told him. After a pause:

"Where'd you get them shoes?"

I gave him the information.

"Hold up your foot!"

I did so. He stepped back, examined the shoe minutely and contemptuously, scratching his head thoughtfully, tilting his high sugar-loaf hat well forward to facilitate the operation, then ejaculated, "Well, I'll be dod derned!" and returned to his wheel.

What occasion there was to be dod derned about it is a thing which is still as much of a mystery to me now as it was then. It must have been all of fifteen minutes— fifteen minutes of dull, homesick silence—before that long horse-face swung round upon me again— and then what a change! It was as red as fire, and every muscle in it was working. Now came this shriek: "Here! You going to set there all day?"

I lit in the middle of the floor, shot there by the electric suddenness of the surprise. As soon as I could get my voice I said apologetically: "I have had no orders, sir."

"You've had no *orders!* My, what a fine bird we are! We must have *orders!* Our father was a *gentleman*—and *we've* been to

Mark Twain portrait (1861)
Mark Twain House
Hartford, Connecticut

Words to Know

furtive (FUR tiv) *adj.*: Sneaky
contemptuously (kuhn TEMP choo uhs lee) *adv.*: Scornfully

school. Yes, *we* are a gentleman, *too*, and got to have *orders!* ORDERS, is it? ORDERS is what you want! Dod dern my skin, *I'll* learn you to swell yourself up and blow around *here* about your dod-derned *orders!* G'way from the wheel!" (I had approached it without knowing it.)

📖 **Read Actively**

Connect with Twain's feelings as he is being questioned by Mr. Brown. How would you feel?

I moved back a step or two and stood as in a dream, all my senses stupefied by this frantic assault.

"What you standing there for? Take that ice-pitcher down to the texas-tender![7] Come, move along, and don't you be all day about it!"

The moment I got back to the pilothouse Brown said: "Here! What was you doing down there all this time?"

"I couldn't find the texas-tender; I had to go all the way to the pantry."

"Derned likely story! Fill up the stove."

I proceeded to do so. He watched me like a cat. Presently he shouted: "Put down that shovel! Derndest numskull I ever saw—ain't even got sense enough to load up a stove."

---

7. **texas-tender:** The waiter in the officers' quarters. On Mississippi steamboats, rooms were named after the states. The officers' area, which was the largest, was named after what was then the largest state, Texas.

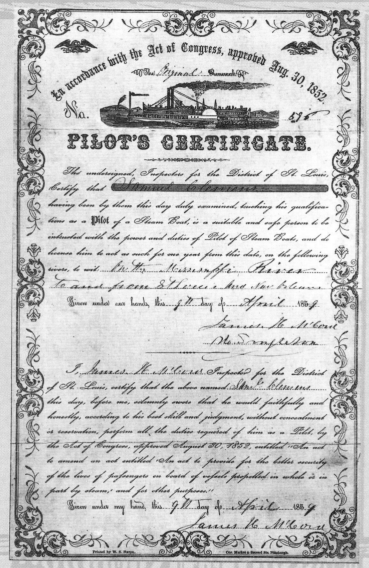

Mark Twain's Pilot's Certificate
Courtesy of the Mariners Museum, Newport News, Virginia

All through the watch this sort of thing went on. Yes, and the subsequent watches were much like it during a stretch of months. As I have said, I soon got the habit of coming on duty with dread. The moment I was in the presence, even in the darkest night, I could feel those yellow eyes upon me, and knew their owner was watching for a pretext to spit out some venom on me. Preliminarily he would say: "Here! Take the wheel."

Two minutes later: "*Where* in the nation you going to? Pull her down! pull her down!"

After another moment: "Say! You going to hold her all day? Let her go—meet her! meet her!"

Then he would jump from the bench, snatch the wheel from me, and meet her himself, pouring out wrath upon me all the time.

Georgie Ritchie was the other pilot's cub. He was having good times now; for his boss, George Ealer, was as kind-hearted as Brown wasn't. Ritchie had steered for Brown the season before; consequently, he knew exactly how to entertain himself and plague me, all by the one operation. Whenever I took the wheel for a moment on Ealer's watch, Ritchie would sit back on the bench and play Brown, with continual ejaculations of "Snatch her! Snatch her! Derndest mudcat I ever saw!" "Here! Where are you going *now?* Going to run over that snag?" "Pull her *down!* Don't you hear me? Pull her *down!*" "There she goes! *Just* as I expected! I *told* you not to cramp that reef. G'way from the wheel!"

So I always had a rough time of it, no matter whose watch it was; and sometimes it seemed to me that Ritchie's good-natured badgering was pretty nearly as aggravating as Brown's dead-earnest nagging.

I often wanted to kill Brown, but this would not answer. A cub had to take everything his boss gave, in the way of vigorous comment and criticism; and we all believed that there was a United States law making it a penitentiary offense to strike or threaten a pilot who was on duty.

Words to Know

stupefied (STOO puh fīd) *adj.*: Stunned
pretext (PRE tekst) *n.*: Excuse
badgering (BAJ er ing) *n.*: Torment

📖 **Read Actively**

Predict how Twain will deal with his feelings toward Brown.

However, I could *imagine* myself killing Brown; there was no law against that; and that was the thing I used always to do the moment I was abed. Instead of going over my river in my mind, as was my duty, I threw business aside for pleasure, and killed Brown. I killed Brown every night for months; not in old, stale, commonplace ways, but in new and picturesque ones—ways that were sometimes surprising for freshness of design and ghastliness of situation and environment.

Brown was *always* watching for a pretext to find fault; and if he could find no plausible pretext, he would invent one. He would scold you for shaving a shore, and for not shaving it; for hugging a bar, and for not hugging it; for "pulling down" when not invited, and for *not* pulling down when not invited; for firing up without orders, and for waiting *for* orders. In a word, it was his invariable rule to find fault with *everything* you did and another invariable rule of his was to throw all his remarks (to you) into the form of an insult.

One day we were approaching New Madrid, bound down and heavily laden. Brown was at one side of the wheel, steering; I was at the other, standing by to "pull down" or "shove up." He cast a furtive glance at me every now and then. I had long ago learned what that meant; viz., he was trying to invent a trap for me. I wondered what shape it was going to take. By and by he stepped back from the wheel and said in his usually snarly way:

"Here! See if you've got gumption enough to round her to."

This was simply *bound* to be a success; nothing could prevent it; for he had never allowed me to round the boat to before; consequently, no matter how I might do the thing, he could find free fault with it. He stood back there with his greedy eye on me, and the result was what might have been foreseen: I lost my head in a quarter of a minute, and didn't know what I was about; I started too early to bring the boat around, but detected a green gleam of joy in Brown's eye, and corrected my mistake.

I started around once more while too high up, but corrected myself again in time. I made other false moves, and still managed to save myself; but at last I grew so confused and anxious that I tumbled into the very worst blunder of all—I got too far *down* before beginning to fetch the boat around. Brown's chance was come.

His face turned red with passion; he made one bound, hurled me across the house with a sweep of his arm, spun the wheel down, and began to pour out a stream of vituperation[8] upon me which lasted till he was out of breath. In the course of this speech he called me all the different kinds of hard names he could think of, and once or twice I thought he was even going to swear—but he had never done that, and he didn't this time. "Dod dern" was the nearest he ventured to the luxury of swearing.

Two trips later I got into serious trouble. Brown was steering; I was "pulling down." My younger brother Henry appeared on the hurricane deck, and shouted to Brown to stop at some landing or other, a mile or so below. Brown gave no intimation that he had heard anything. But that was his way: he never con-

---

8. **vituperation** (vi too pe RAY shuhn) *n.*: Abusive language.

descended to take notice of an underclerk. The wind was blowing; Brown was deaf (although he always pretended he wasn't), and I very much doubted if he had heard the order. If I had had two heads, I would have spoken; but as I had only one, it seemed judicious to take care of it; so I kept still.

Presently, sure enough, we went sailing by that plantation. Captain Klinefelter appeared on the deck, and said: "Let her come around, sir, let her come around. Didn't Henry tell you to land here?"

"*No*, sir!"

"I sent him up to do it."

"He *did* come up; and that's all the good it done, the dod-derned fool. He never said anything."

"Didn't *you* hear him?" asked the captain of me.

Of course I didn't want to be mixed up in this business, but there was no way to avoid it; so I said: "Yes, sir."

I knew what Brown's next remark would be, before he uttered it. It was: "Shut your mouth! You never heard anything of the kind."

I closed my mouth, according to instructions. An hour later Henry entered the pilot-house, unaware of what had been going on. He was a thoroughly inoffensive boy, and I was sorry to see him come, for I knew Brown would have no pity on him. Brown began,

Looking down the Mississippi River at Hannibal, Missouri
George L. Crosby
Mark Twain Home and Museum, Hannibal, Missouri

straightway: "Here! Why didn't you tell me we'd got to land at that plantation?"

"I did tell you, Mr. Brown."

"It's a lie!"

I said: "You lie, yourself. He did tell you."

Brown glared at me in unaffected surprise; and for as much as a moment he was entirely speechless; then he shouted to me: "I'll attend to your case in a half a minute!" then to Henry, "And you leave the pilothouse; out with you!"

It was pilot law, and must be obeyed. The boy started out, and even had his foot on the upper step outside the door, when Brown, with a sudden access of fury, picked up a ten-pound lump of coal and sprang after him; but I was between, with a heavy stool, and I hit Brown a good honest blow which stretched him out.

I had committed the crime of crimes—I had lifted my hand against a pilot on duty! I supposed I was booked for the penitentiary sure, and couldn't be booked any surer if I went on and squared my long account with this person while I had the chance; consequently I stuck to him and pounded him with my fists a considerable time. I do not know how long, the pleasure of it probably made it seem longer than it really was; but in the end he struggled free and jumped up and sprang to the wheel: a very natural solicitude, for, all this time, here was this steamboat tearing down the river at the rate of fifteen miles an hour and nobody at the helm!

📖 **Read Actively**

Visualize what is happening to the boat when the author scuffles with Mr. Brown.

However, Eagle Bend was two miles wide at this bank-full stage, and correspondingly long and deep: and the boat was steering herself straight down the middle and taking no chances. Still, that was only luck—a body *might* have found her charging into the woods.

Perceiving at a glance that the *Pennsylvania* was in no danger, Brown gathered up the big spyglass, war-club fashion, and ordered me out of the pilothouse with more than ordinary bluster. But I was not afraid of him now; so, instead of going, I tarried, and criticized his grammar. I reformed his ferocious speeches for him, and put them into good English, calling his attention to the advantage of pure English over the dialect of the collieries[9] whence he was extracted. He could have done his part to admiration in a crossfire of mere vituperation, of course; but he was not equipped for this species of controversy; so he presently laid aside his glass and took the wheel, muttering and shaking his head; and I retired to the bench. The racket had brought everybody to the hurricane deck, and I trembled when I saw the old captain looking up from amid the crowd. I said to myself, "Now I *am* done for!" for although, as a rule, he was so fatherly and indulgent toward the boat's family, and so patient of minor shortcomings, he could be stern enough when the fault was worth it.

I tried to imagine what he *would* do to a cub pilot who had been guilty of such a crime as mine, committed on a boat guard-deep[10] with costly freight and alive with passengers. Our watch was nearly ended. I thought I would go and hide somewhere till I got a chance to slide ashore. So I slipped out of the pilothouse, and down the steps, and around to the texas-door, when the captain confronted me! I dropped my head, and he stood over me in silence a moment or two, then said impressively: "Follow me."

I dropped into his wake; he led the way to his parlor in the forward end of the texas. We were alone now. He closed the afterdoor, then moved slowly to the forward one and closed that. He sat down; I stood before him. He looked at me some little time, then said: "So you have been fighting Mr. Brown?"

I answered meekly: "Yes, sir."

"Do you know that that is a very serious matter?"

"Yes, sir."

"Are you aware that this boat was plowing down the river fully five minutes with no one at the wheel?"

---

9. **collieries** (KOL yur eez) *n.*: Coal mines.

10. **guard-deep:** Here, a wooden frame protecting the paddle wheel.

Words to Know

intimation (in tuh MAY shuhn) *n.*: Hint

judicious (joo DI shuhs) *adj.*: Careful

"Yes, sir."

"Did you strike him first?"

"Yes, sir."

"What with?"

"A stool, sir."

"Hard?"

"Middling, sir."

"Did it knock him down?"

"He—he fell, sir."

"Did you follow it up? Did you do anything further?"

"Yes, sir."

"What did you do?"

"Pounded him, sir."

"Pounded him?"

"Yes, sir."

"Did you pound him much? that is, severely?"

"One might call it that, sir, maybe."

"I'm deuced glad of it! Hark ye, never mention that I said that. You have been guilty of a great crime; and don't you ever be guilty of it again, on this boat. *But*—lay for him ashore! Give him a good sound thrashing, do you hear? I'll pay the expenses. Now go—and mind you, not a word of this to anybody. Clear out with you! You've been guilty of a great crime, you whelp!"[11]

I slid out, happy with the sense of a close shave and a mighty deliverance; and I heard him laughing to himself and slapping his fat thighs after I had closed his door.

When Brown came off watch he went straight to the captain, who was talking with

Read Actively

Respond to the resolution of the conflict between the author and Mr. Brown. Were you surprised?

some passengers on the boiler deck, and demanded that I be put ashore in New Orleans—and added: "I'll never turn a wheel on this boat again while that cub stays."

The captain said: "But he needn't come round when you are on watch, Mr. Brown."

"I won't even stay on the same boat with him. *One* of us has got to go ashore."

"Very well," said the captain, "let it be yourself," and resumed his talk with the passengers.

11. **whelp** (WELP) *n.*: A young dog or puppy: here, a disrespectful young man.

During the brief remainder of the trip I knew how an emancipated slave feels, for I was an emancipated slave myself. While we lay at landings I listened to George Ealer's flute, or to his readings from his two Bibles, that is to say, Goldsmith and Shakespeare, or I played chess with him—and would have beaten him sometimes, only he always took back his last move and ran the game out differently.

Respond

- What did you think of Twain's actions with regard to Mr. Brown?
- List the pros and cons of Twain's actions under the circumstances.

Mark Twain (1835–1910)

First Job: At the age of eleven, Twain became an apprentice typesetter for local Missouri newspapers. Later he fulfilled his boyhood dream and became a steamboat pilot on the Mississippi River.

Adventures: Twain panned for gold and silver in Nevada with his brother, in an unsuccessful venture. He later wrote about this adventure in his book *Roughing It.* While in Nevada he fled town when a rival journalist challenged him to a duel.

Famous Firsts: Twain owned the first telephone installed in a private house and was the first professional writer to use a typewriter.

Fashion Statements: In his later years, Twain wore only white clothes year-round and designed his own shirts, which buttoned down the back.

Activities
MAKE MEANING

 Explore Your Reading

Look Back (Recall)

1. What terms does Twain use to describe Mr. Brown?
2. What finally makes the conflict between Twain and Mr. Brown break into violence?

Think It Over (Interpret)

3. Why do you think Mr. Brown treats cub pilots as he does?
4. What do you think the author learned from his experiences with Mr. Brown?

Going Beyond (Apply)

5. Is it ever appropriate to resolve conflicts with violence? Explain.

 Develop Reading and Literary Skills

Analyze Conflict Between Characters

As you have seen, the major conflict in "Cub Pilot on the Mississippi" turns on a problem between Twain, the apprentice, and Mr. Brown, his teacher. Conflicts between characters can be resolved in many ways. One can win and one can lose, the opponents can agree to a compromise, or circumstances can change to make the conflict vanish.

Analyze the conflict in "Cub Pilot on the Mississippi" using the list you made as you read. Think of the conflicts between Brown and Mark Twain as a seesaw.

1. List three points in the narrative where Mr. Brown and Twain are in opposition.
2. Draw a seesaw to indicate who is "up" and who is "down" in the conflict at each of those points.
3. Explain how each incident is resolved.
4. Is any part of the conflict unresolved? Explain.

Ideas for Writing

Conflicts between personalities may not be easily resolved. Consider whether the conflict between Mark Twain and Mr. Brown is resolvable.

Persuasive Paper Write a persuasive paper agreeing or disagreeing with Twain's means of resolving his conflict with Mr. Brown. If you agree with what he did, give examples and reasons from the narrative to support your opinion. If you oppose what he did, give reasons for your opinion and offer alternatives.

Narration and Dialogue Describe a future meeting between Twain and Brown. Set up the scene with narration, and then write a passage in dialogue as they talk to each other. Use quotation marks where appropriate. Make the characters sound as they do in the selection.

Ideas for Projects

Mark Twain Day Plan a Mark Twain Day. Volunteer "Mark Twains" can read aloud or perform passages from works by Twain. Others can prepare small-group discussions or illustrations of riverboat travel and other aspects of nineteenth-century life. Culminate the celebration by displaying the best design for a riverboat stamp or portrait of Twain. [Social Studies Link; Art Link]

Oral Report With a group, read a biography of Mark Twain and two or more other books that describe life on the Mississippi in the nineteenth century. Prepare a report about river life. Work with classmates to find illustrations for the report or to create a map of the Mississippi River in the nineteenth century. [Social Studies Link]

How Am I Doing?

Respond to these questions in your journal:
What have I learned from Mark Twain's story about dealing with difficult people?

How can my understanding of conflict help me in my reading?

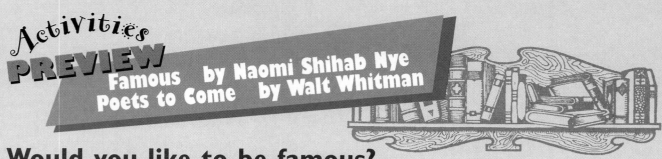

Would you like to be famous?
Why or why not?

Reach Into Your Background

How would you define "fame," and what makes someone "famous"? Who would you name as the three most famous living people in the United States at this moment? Why?

- Compare your list of famous people with a partner's list. Identify what makes one person more famous than another.
- In a group, discuss the advantages and disadvantages of fame. Tell whether you would want to be famous or not. Why?

Read Actively
Analyze Ideas in Poems

Poems do many things: describe breathtaking pictures, create spectacular sound effects, make startling comparisons. Besides communicating strong emotions, poems express ideas or points of view. Most often, however, poets don't express their ideas directly. Instead, they leave it up to the reader to think about the ideas suggested by the images and comparisons in the poem.

As you read these two poems, think about the ideas or points each speaker is making—particularly the ideas about reputation and fame. Take notes in your journal.

Famous
NAOMI SHIHAB NYE

The river is famous to the fish.

The loud voice is famous to silence,
which knew it would inherit the earth
before anybody said so.

5 The cat sleeping on the fence is famous to the birds
watching him from the birdhouse.

The tear is famous, briefly, to the cheek.

The idea you carry close to your bosom
is famous to your bosom.

10 The boot is famous to the earth,
more famous than the dress shoe,
which is famous only to floors.

The bent photograph is famous to the one who
  carries it
and not at all famous to the one who is pictured.

15 I want to be famous to shuffling men
who smile while crossing streets,
sticky children in grocery lines,
famous as the one who smiled back.

I want to be famous in the way a pulley is famous,
20 or a buttonhole, not because it did anything
  spectacular,
but because it never forgot what it could do.

Naomi Shihab Nye
(1952–   )

    Naomi Shihab Nye's father emigrated from Palestine and settled in St. Louis, where he and his wife ran stores specializing in imported goods. When Naomi was fourteen, the family moved to Jerusalem to be near her father's Arab relatives. She recalls the relocation as a great disruption in her life—she missed the family piano and her mother's unusual red stove.

    Nevertheless, the family's year in Jerusalem enabled Naomi to get in touch with roots of her heritage that her father had left behind. She learned how to say "I love you" in Armenian and discovered that Shihab, her middle name, means "shooting star".

Words to Know

shuffling (SHUHF ling) *adj.*: A slight dragging of feet in walking (line 15)

Poets to Come

Walt Whitman

Walt Whitman
The Granger Collection, New York

Poets to come! orators, singers, musicians to come!
Not to-day is to justify me and answer what I am for,
But you, a new brood, native, athletic, continental, greater than before known,
Arouse! for you must justify me.

5   I myself but write one or two indicative words for the future,
I but advance a moment only to wheel and hurry back in the darkness.

I am a man who, sauntering along without fully stopping, turns a
    casual look upon you and then averts his face,
Leaving it to you to prove and define it,
10 Expecting the main things from you.

Respond

- Both poems use unconventional images to talk about fame. Which image of fame is your favorite?
- In your journal, explain what your favorite image from these poems says about fame.

Words to Know

orators (OR uh terz) *n.*: People who make public speeches (line 1)
indicative (in DIK uh tiv) *adj.*: Giving a suggestion; showing (line 5)
sauntering (SAWN ter ing) *v.*: Walking slowly and confidently (line 7)

Walt Whitman (1819–1892)

In the preface to his volume of poetry *Leaves of Grass,* Walt Whitman expresses many ideas about what makes a true poet:

- As the poet "sees the farthest he has the most faith. His thoughts are the hymns of the praise of things."
- The poet's "spirit responds to his country's spirit. . . . he incarnates its geography and natural life and rivers and lakes."
- "The proof of a poet is that his country absorbs him as affectionately as he has absorbed it."
- "He is a seer. . . he is individual. . . . he is complete in himself. . . . the others are as good as he, only he sees it and they do not."

Activities

MAKE MEANING

Explore Your Reading

Look Back (Recall)

1. According to the last lines of "Famous," what does the speaker want to do for the children in grocery lines?
2. In "Poets to Come," what does the speaker expect future poets to do?

Think It Over (Interpret)

3. Why does the speaker in "Famous" compare fame to that of such ordinary things as pulleys and buttonholes?
4. What does the speaker in "Poets to Come" mean when he asks future artists to "justify" him?

Go Beyond (Apply)

5. What things would these poets say are more important than being famous? What things would *you* say are more important?

Develop Reading and Literary Skills

Understand Themes in Poems

The ideas, images, and comparisons presented in a poem all contribute to the expression of a **theme,** the poem's central idea. For example, in "Famous," Naomi Shihab Nye asks us to imagine what floors think of dress shoes. Her image makes the point that dress shoes wouldn't dream of being boots and tromping outdoors on ground; they're indoor creatures perfectly suited to floors. This unusual image expresses an idea, or theme, about fame.

1. List the images in lines 5–6 and 13–15 of "Famous." What idea about fame does each of these images express?
2. Visualize the actions of the speaker in lines 5–10 of "Poets to Come." What do these actions suggest about the idea of fame?
3. In your own words, state the theme of each poem.

Ideas for Writing

Some people seek out fame, and sometimes fame finds people. Explore what fame does to a person's life.

Biographical Essay Choose a famous person and write a biographical essay that analyzes what made him or her famous. You will probably need to research some background material. When did this person become famous, and why? What effects, if any, does fame seem to have had on his or her life?

Book Jacket Imagine that you have become a celebrity and that you have just written your autobiography telling how you became famous. Write a bookjacket "blurb" that describes your life and entices people to read your book.

Ideas for Projects

Fame Gallery Imagine that you are a curator planning an American waxworks museum. Select five people whose images you would like to display. Use photos or drawings and write labels that highlight the admirable characteristics of each person. Display your gallery on a bulletin board, or create a diorama display.

Fan Club Working with a partner, choose a famous person you admire and regard as a role model. Form a two-person fan club. Collect photographs, newspaper and magazine clippings, and other items about your subject and organize them in a scrapbook. Write a fan letter to him or her and share any response you receive with the class.

How Am I Doing?

Jot in your journal responses to one or both of these questions:

How have my ideas about fame changed from reading these poems?

Which piece of my work best expresses a theme?

Activities
PREVIEW
A Shot at It   by Esmeralda Santiago

What will people do to achieve success?

Reach Into Your Background

If you ever auditioned for a play or show, or were interviewed for admission to a school or special program, you know what these experiences were like and how you felt beforehand. If you've never participated in an audition or interview, how would you *expect* to feel, knowing that you were about to go to one?

- With a small group of students, discuss how to behave and what to say during an interview for a school or a job.
- With a partner, take turns role-playing interviewer and interviewee for a position of club president. Decide what club you are applying to and what qualifications you have for the position.

Read Actively
Analyze a Narrator's Viewpoint

"A Shot at It" tells about an audition, a kind of interview for a special school: the School for the Performing Arts in New York City. It is a first-person account, which means the **narrator** (the person telling the story) is telling about an event in her own life. When you read a first-person account, you share the narrator's views on the situations and events she tells about.

Identify the narrator's views by listing her concerns and anticipations as you read. Use a chart like this one to keep a record of your observations as you read.

Situation or event	What the narrator says	What I see

A SHOT AT IT

ESMERALDA SANTIAGO

While Francisco was still alive, we had moved to Ellery Street. That meant I had to change schools, so Mami walked me to P.S. 33, where I would attend ninth grade. The first week I was there I was given a series of tests that showed that even though I couldn't speak English very well, I read and wrote it at the tenth-grade level. So they put me in 9-3, with the smart kids.

One morning, Mr. Barone, a guidance counsellor, called me to his office. He was short, with a big head and large hazel eyes under shapely eyebrows. His nose was long and round at the tip. He dressed in browns and yellows and often perched his tortoiseshell glasses on his forehead, as if he had another set of eyes up there.

"So," he pushed his glasses up, "what do you want to be when you grow up?"

"I don't know."

He shuffled through some papers. "Let's see here . . . you're fourteen, is that right?"

"Yes, sir."

"And you've never thought about what you want to be?"

When I was very young, I wanted to be a *jíbara*.[1] When I was older, I wanted to be a cartographer,[2] then a topographer.[3] But since we'd come to Brooklyn, I'd not thought about the future much.

"No, sir."

He pulled his glasses down to where they belonged and shuffled through the papers again.

"Do you have any hobbies?" I didn't know what he meant. "Hobbies, hobbies," he flailed his hands, as if he were juggling, "things you like to do after school."

"Ah, yes." I tried to imagine what I did at home that might qualify as a hobby. "I like to read."

He seemed disappointed. "Yes, we know that about you." He pulled out a paper and stared at it. "One of the tests we gave you was an aptitude test. It tells us what kinds of things you might be good at. The tests show that you would be good at helping people. Do you like to help people?"

I was afraid to contradict the tests. "Yes, sir."

"There's a high school we can send you where you can study biology and chemistry which will prepare you for a career in nursing."

I screwed up my face. He consulted the papers again.

"You would also do well in communications. Teaching maybe."

I remembered Miss Brown standing in front of a classroom full of rowdy teenagers, some of them taller than she was.

"I don't like to teach."

Mr. Barone pushed his glasses up again and leaned over the stack of papers on his desk. "Why don't you think about it and get back to me," he said, closing the folder with my name across the top. He put his hand flat on it, as if squeezing something out. "You're a smart girl, Esmeralda. Let's try to get you into an academic school so that you have a shot at college."

On the way home, I walked with another new ninth grader, Yolanda. She had been in New York for three years but knew as little English as I did. We spoke in Spanglish, a combination of English and Spanish in which we hopped from one language to the other depending on which word came first.

"*Te preguntó el* Mr. Barone, you know, *lo que querías hacer* when you grow up?" I asked.

"*Sí, pero,* I didn't know. *¿Y tú?*"

1. *jíbara* (HEE bah ruh) *n*.: A poor farmer.
2. **cartographer** (kar TAHG ruh fer) *n*.: A mapmaker.
3. **topographer** (tuh PAHG ruh fer) *n*.: A person who makes maps showing the surface features of a place.

"*Yo tampoco.* He said, *que* I like to help people. *Pero*, you know, *a mí no me gusta mucho la gente.*" When she heard me say I didn't like people much, Yolanda looked at me from the corner of her eye, waiting to become the exception.

By the time I said it, she had dashed up the stairs of her building. She didn't wave as she ducked in, and the next day she wasn't friendly. I walked around the rest of the day in embarrassed isolation, knowing that somehow I had given myself away to the only friend I'd made at Junior High School 33. I had to either take back my words or live with the consequences of stating what was becoming the truth. I'd never said that to anyone, not even to myself. It was an added weight, but I wasn't about to trade it for companionship.

📖 **Read Actively**

Connect with Esmeralda's sense of being an outsider.

A few days later, Mr. Barone called me back to his office.

"Well?" Tiny green flecks burned around the black pupils of his hazel eyes.

The night before, Mami had called us into the living room. On the television "fifty of America's most beautiful girls" paraded in ruffled tulle dresses before a tinsel waterfall.

"Aren't they lovely?" Mami murmured, as the girls, escorted by boys in uniform, floated by the camera, twirled, and disappeared behind a screen to the strains of a waltz and an announcer's dramatic voice calling their names, ages, and states. Mami sat mesmerized through the whole pageant.

"I'd like to be a model," I said to Mr. Barone.

He stared at me, pulled his glasses down from his forehead, looked at the papers inside the folder with my name on it, and glared. "A model?" His voice was gruff, as if he were more comfortable yelling at people than talking to them.

"I want to be on television."

"Oh, then you want to be an actress," in a tone that said this was only a slight improvement over my first career choice. We stared at one another for a few seconds. He pushed his glasses up to his forehead again and reached for a book on the shelf in back of him. "I only know of one school that trains actresses, but we've never sent them a student from here."

Performing Arts, the write-up said, was an academic, as opposed to a vocational, public school that trained students wishing to pursue a career in theater, music, and dance.

"It says here that you have to audition." He stood up and held the book closer to the faint gray light coming through the narrow window high on his wall. "Have you ever performed in front of an audience?"

"I was announcer in my school show in Puerto Rico," I said. "And I recite poetry. There, not here."

He closed the book and held it against his chest. His right index finger thumped a rhythm on his lower lip. "Let me call them and find out exactly what you need to do. Then we can talk some more."

I left his office strangely happy, confident that something good had just happened, not knowing exactly what.

"I'm not afraid . . . I'm not afraid . . . I'm not afraid." Every day I walked home from school repeating those words. The broad streets and sidewalks that had impressed me so on the first day we had arrived had become as familiar as the dirt road from Macún to the highway. Only my curiosity about the people who lived behind these walls ended where the façades of the buildings opened into dark hallways or locked doors. Nothing good, I imagined, could be happening inside if so many locks had to be breached to go in or step out.

It was on these tense walks home from school that I decided I had to get out of Brooklyn. Mami had chosen this as our home,

Words to Know

aptitude (AP tuh tood) *n.*: Inborn skill
mesmerized (MEZ muh rīzd) *adj.*: Almost hypnotized
vocational (voh CAY shuhn uhl) *adj.*: Aimed at teaching a trade rather than preparing for college
façades (fuh SAHDZ) *n.*: Fronts of buildings

and just like every other time we'd moved, I'd had to go along with her because I was a child who had no choice. But I wasn't willing to go along with her on this one.

"How can people live like this?" I shrieked once, desperate to run across a field, to feel grass under my feet instead of pavement.

"Like what?" Mami asked, looking around our apartment, the kitchen and living room crisscrossed with sagging lines of drying diapers and bedclothes.

"Everyone on top of each other. No room to do anything. No air."

"Do you want to go back to Macún, to live like savages, with no electricity, no toilets . . ."

"At least you could step outside every day without somebody trying to kill you."

"Ay, Negi, stop exaggerating!"

"I hate my life!" I yelled.

"Then do something about it," she yelled back.

📖 **Read Actively**

Connect with Esmeralda's desire to change her circumstances. How will going to the High School for the Performing Arts help her?

Until Mr. Barone showed me the listing for Performing Arts High School, I hadn't known what to do.

"The auditions are in less than a month. You have to learn a monologue, which you will perform in front of a panel. If you do well, and your grades here are good, you might get into the school."

Mr. Barone took charge of preparing me for my audition to Performing Arts. He selected a speech from *The Silver Cord*, a play by Sidney Howard, first performed in 1926, but whose action took place in a New York drawing room circa 1905.

"Mr. Gatti, the English teacher," he said, "will coach you. . . . And Mrs. Johnson will talk to you about what to wear and things like that."

I was to play Christina, a young married woman confronting her mother-in-law. I learned the monologue phonetically from Mr. Gatti. It opened with "You belong to a type that's very common in this country, Mrs. Phelps—a type of self-centered, self-pitying, son-devouring tigress, with unmentionable proclivities suppressed on the side."

"We don't have time to study the meaning of every word," Mr. Gatti said. "Just make sure you pronounce every word correctly."

Mrs. Johnson, who taught Home Economics, called me to her office.

"Is that how you enter a room?" she asked the minute I came in. "Try again, only this time, don't barge in. Step in slowly, head up, back straight, a nice smile on your face. That's it." I took a deep breath and waited. "Now sit. No, not like that. Don't just plop down. Float down to the chair with your knees together." She demonstrated, and I copied her. "That's better. What do you do with your hands? No, don't hold your chin like that; it's not ladylike. Put your hands on your lap, and leave them there. Don't use them so much when you talk."

I sat stiff as a cutout while Mrs. Johnson and Mr. Barone asked me questions they thought the panel at Performing Arts would ask.

"Where are you from?"

"Puerto Rico."

"No," Mrs. Johnson said, "Porto Rico. Keep your *r*'s soft. Try again."

"Do you have any hobbies?" Mr. Barone asked. Now I knew what to answer.

"I enjoy dancing and the movies."

"Why do you want to come to this school?"

Mrs. Johnson and Mr. Barone had worked on my answer if this question should come up.

"I would like to study at Performing Arts because of its academic program and so that I may be trained as an actress."

"Very good, very good!" Mr. Barone rubbed his hands together, twinkled his eyes at Mrs. Johnson. "I think we have a shot at this."

"Remember," Mrs. Johnson said, "when you shop for your audition dress, look for something very simple in dark colors."

Mami bought me a red plaid wool jumper with a crisp white shirt, my first pair of stockings, and penny loafers. The night before, she rolled up my hair in pink curlers that cut into my scalp and made it hard to sleep. For the occasion, I was allowed to wear eye makeup and a little lipstick.

"You look so grown up!" Mami said, her voice sad but happy, as I twirled in front of her and Tata.

"Toda una señorita," Tata said, her eyes misty.

We set out for the audition on an overcast January morning heavy with the threat of snow.

📖 **Read Actively**

Predict how Esmeralda's audition will go.

"Why couldn't you choose a school close to home?" Mami grumbled as we got on the train to Manhattan. I worried that even if I were accepted, she wouldn't let me go because it was so far from home, one hour each way by subway. But in spite of her complaints, she was proud that I was good enough to be considered for such a famous school. And she actually seemed excited that I would be leaving the neighborhood.

"You'll be exposed to a different class of people," she assured me, and I felt the force of her ambition without knowing exactly what she meant.

Three women sat behind a long table in a classroom where the desks and chairs had been pushed against a wall. As I entered I held my head up and smiled, and then I floated down to the chair in front of them, clasped my hands on my lap, and smiled some more.

"Good morning," said the tall one with hair the color of sand. She was big boned and solid, with intense blue eyes, a generous mouth, and soothing hands with short fingernails. She was dressed in shades of beige from head to toe and wore no makeup and no jewelry except for the gold chain that held her glasses just above her full bosom. Her voice was rich, modulated, each word pronounced as if she were inventing it.

Next to her sat a very small woman with very high heels. Her cropped hair was pouffed around her face, with bangs brushing the tips of her long false lashes, her huge dark brown eyes were thickly lined in black all around, and her small mouth was carefully drawn in and painted cerise. Her suntanned face turned toward me with the innocent curiosity of a lively baby. She was dressed in black, with many gold chains around her neck, big earrings, sev-

eral bracelets, and large stone rings on the fingers of both hands.

The third woman was tall, small boned, thin, but shapely. Her dark hair was pulled flat against her skull into a knot in back of her head. Her face was all angles and light, with fawnlike dark brown eyes, a straight nose, full lips painted just a shade pinker than their natural color. Silky forest green cuffs peeked out from the sleeves of her burgundy suit. Diamond studs winked from perfect earlobes.

I had dreamed of this moment for several weeks. More than anything, I wanted to impress the panel with my talent, so that I would be accepted into Performing Arts and leave Brooklyn every day. And, I hoped, one day I would never go back.

But the moment I faced these three impeccably groomed women, I forgot my English and Mrs. Johnson's lessons on how to behave like a lady. In the agony of trying to answer their barely comprehensible questions, I jabbed my hands here and there, forming words with my fingers because the words refused to leave my mouth.

"Why don't you let us hear your monologue now?" the woman with the dangling glasses asked softly.

I stood up abruptly, and my chair clattered onto its side two feet from where I stood. I picked it up, wishing with all my strength that a thunderbolt would strike me dead to ashes on the spot.

"It's all right," she said. "Take a breath. We know you're nervous."

I closed my eyes and breathed deeply, walked to the middle of the room and began my monologue.

"Ju bee lonh 2 a type dats berry cómo in dis kuntree, Mees-sees Felps. A type off self-cent red self pee tee in sun de boring tie gress

Words to Know

impeccably (im PEK uh blee) *adv.*: Flawlessly
pantomime (PAN toh mīm) *n.*: A performance without words

wid on men shon ah ball pro klee bee tees on de side."

In spite of Mr. Gatti's reminders that I should speak slowly and enunciate every word, even if I didn't understand it, I recited my three-minute monologue in one minute flat.

The small woman's long lashes seemed to have grown with amazement. The elegant woman's serene face twitched with controlled laughter. The tall one dressed in beige smiled sweetly.

"Thank you, dear," she said. "Could you wait outside for a few moments?"

I resisted the urge to curtsy. The long hallway had narrow wainscoting[4] halfway up to the high ceiling. Single bulb lamps hung from long cords, creating yellow puddles of light on the polished brown linoleum tile. A couple of girls my age sat on straight chairs next to their mothers, waiting their turn. They looked up as I came out and the door shut behind me. Mami stood up from her chair at the end of the hall. She looked as scared as I felt.

"What happened?"

"Nothing," I mumbled, afraid that if I began telling her about it, I would break into tears in front of the other people, whose eyes followed me and Mami as we walked to the EXIT sign. "I have to wait here a minute."

"Did they say anything?"

"No. I'm just supposed to wait."

We leaned against the wall. Across from us there was a bulletin board with newspaper clippings about former students. On the ragged edge, a neat person had printed in blue ink, "P.A." and the year the actor, dancer, or musician had graduated. I closed my eyes and tried to picture myself on that bulletin board, with "P.A. '66" across the top.

The door at the end of the hall opened, and the woman in beige poked her head out.

Read Actively

Ask yourself whether or not the women who are interviewing Esmeralda see her sympathetically.

"Esmeralda?"

"*Sí*, I mean, here." I raised my hand.

She led me into the room. There was another girl in there, whom she introduced as Bonnie, a junior at the school.

"Do you know what a pantomime is?" the woman asked. I nodded. "You and Bonnie are sisters decorating a Christmas tree."

Bonnie looked a lot like Juanita Marín, whom I had last seen in Macún four years earlier. We decided where the invisible Christmas tree would be, and we sat on the floor and pretended we were taking decorations out of boxes and hanging them on the branches.

My family had never had a Christmas tree, but I remembered how once I had helped Papi wind colored lights around the eggplant bush that divided our land from Doña Ana's. We started at the bottom and wound the wire with tiny red bulbs around and around until we ran out; then Papi plugged another cord to it and we kept going until the branches hung heavy with light and the bush looked like it was on fire.

Before long I had forgotten where I was, and that the tree didn't exist and Bonnie was not my sister. She pretended to hand me a very delicate ball, and just before I took it, she made like it fell to the ground and shattered. I was petrified that Mami would come in and yell at us for breaking her favorite decoration. Just as I began to pick up the tiny fragments of nonexistent crystal, a voice broke in. "Thank you." Bonnie got up, smiled, and went out.

---

4. **wainscoting** (WAYN skoht ing) *n.:* Paneled wood trim.

The elegant woman stretched her hand out for me to shake. "We will notify your school in a few weeks. It was very nice to meet you."

I shook hands all around then backed out of the room in a fog, silent, as if the pantomime had taken my voice and the urge to speak.

On the way home Mami kept asking what had happened, and I kept mumbling, "Nothing. Nothing happened," ashamed that, after all the hours of practice with Mrs. Johnson, Mr. Barone, and Mr. Gatti, after the expense of new clothes and shoes, after Mami had to take a day off from work to take me into Manhattan, after all that, I had failed the audition and would never, ever, get out of Brooklyn.

ACT IV
June 1967

SCHOOL OF PERFORMING ARTS
Division of
High School Music and Art
120 West 46th Street
New York 36, New York
Louis K. Wechsler, Principal
Edward T. Koehler, Teacher in Charge

Respond

- Would you have gone to the audition if you were Esmeralda? Why or why not?
- Jot down in your journal the risks you would take to achieve an important goal.

JONAH AND THE WHALE
(Act III, Scene 1)
by James Bridie
CAST
(in order of appearance)

Euodias .... Margo Chan
Sophereth .... Sara Krupenia
Bilshan .... Northern Calloway
Eshtemoa .... Ellen Lerner
Ziz .... Beth Launer
Zaza .... Noreen McCutchen
Tola .... Esmeralda Santiago
Shiphrah .... Deborah Henriquez
Hadadezer .... Roanne Genge
Jonah .... William Beckwith
Place: The balcony of the Hotel Baal, Nineveh. Afternoon. Time: 825 B.C.
By arrangement with Samuel French, Inc.

Esmeralda Santiago grew up in Puerto Rico with seven brothers and sisters. As a child she learned the correct way to eat a guava and would listen to the sound of the tree frogs in the mango groves at night. Then her family moved to New York City, where she struggled to fit into a new world—and learn a new language.

Santiago fulfilled her dream of being accepted into the city's High School for the Performing Arts. She went on to Harvard University, graduating with highest honors. Her first book, *When I Was Puerto Rican,* captures her childhood in Puerto Rico and her difficult transition to life in the United States.

Activities

MAKE MEANING

Explore Your Reading

Look Back (Recall)

1. How does Esmeralda prepare for the audition?
2. What happens at the audition?

Think It Over (Interpret)

3. Why does Esmeralda tell Yolanda that she doesn't like people much?
4. How would going to the High School of Performing Arts get Esmeralda out of Brooklyn? Why does she want to leave?
5. Why does Esmeralda believe that she has failed the audition?

Go Beyond (Apply)

6. What are the effects of having an ambition or a dream that seems almost impossible to achieve? Explain.

Develop Reading and Literary Skills

Make Judgments About the Narrator

In a first-person account, the **narrator** (the person telling the story) presents a view of events in his or her own life. As you read, you develop feelings and opinions about this person. You form **judgments**—informed opinions and observations—about the person, based on the narrator's words and actions and the way he or she relates to other people.

In "A Shot at It," the narrator creates a portrait of herself as she tells about her audition. Look back at the chart you made as you read, and use the information to answer these questions about Esmeralda:

1. What does Esmeralda reveal about herself? Which of her actions show these qualities?
2. What observations can you make about Esmeralda's character? What statements or actions illustrate these points?
3. What is Esmeralda's point in telling her account of the audition? Explain.

Ideas for Writing

As in Esmeralda's narrative, sometimes it takes daring to shape the course of your life.

Persuasive Essay Write an essay that argues whether or not Esmeralda should be admitted into the High School for the Performing Arts. Do you think she is talented? Would she be happier there than at her school in Brooklyn? Use evidence from the selection to back up your opinions.

Feature Article Identify a local person in a role or career that you are interested in pursuing. Interview him or her about the requirements needed for that role or career. Write up the interview as a feature article for your school newspaper.

Ideas for Projects

Career Resource Box Work with a group to create a career box. Focus on careers you think will interest your classmates. For each career, research the requirements, expected earnings, opportunities, and other benefits. Write the information on file cards and organize the cards alphabetically in a box. Share the career resource box with the class.

Career Road Map Create a career road map for yourself. Talk with former students, parents, teachers, and guidance counselors who can guide you to map out a four-year career plan that will prepare you to make choices in high school and beyond. Outline your Road Map and keep it in your portfolio. [Social Studies Link]

How Am I Doing?

Take a moment to write responses to these questions:

What do I have to keep in mind when reading first-person accounts?

What have I learned about steps I can take to prepare for a career?

What is *your* dream job?

Reach Into Your Background

Hobbies and other activities you enjoy might lead someday to a career. Consider some of the possibilities. For example, a passion for computer games might lead to a career designing computer programs. A mania for shopping might develop into a career in merchandising. A need for having the last word might make a good lawyer.

- Discuss career interests with a small group. Suggest several possible careers for each person, based on his or her interests.
- Write in your journal about someone you know who works in a career you might like.

Read Actively
Read for Main Idea and Support

You can learn about both hobbies and careers by reading nonfiction articles—pieces of writing that tell about real people, places, and events. To get the most out of any nonfiction article, look for its **main idea**—the central point the writer is trying to make. For example, a writer might focus on how rewarding a particular career can be. Look also for the **support**—ideas, facts, and details—that a writer offers for his or her main idea. Think about whether the writer offers enough support for his or her main idea.

As you read this article, look for the main idea the author is expressing. Note in your journal the article's main idea, along with details and examples that support it.

LEGO

David Owen

Growing up in Queens in the sixties and seventies, Francie Berger knew exactly what she wanted from life: more Lego building bricks. She received her first set, a gift from her parents, when she was three. Gradually, she added to her holdings. She liked to build houses, and she wished that she could build bigger ones. As a teen-ager, she began writing to Lego Systems, Inc., the American division of the toy's Danish manufacturer, to ask if she could order, say, two million standard red bricks. The company said that she could not. In college—where she majored in architecture, figuring that building real houses was the adult occupation that came closest to her favorite activity—she wrote more letters. At some point, it occurred to her that she might be able to get a job at Lego itself. She began calling the company on a monthly basis, and she once dropped by its headquarters, in Enfield, Connecticut. "By then," Berger recalls, "they knew who I was." The person who was dispatched to get rid of her told her to send a résumé, by mail, after graduation. Undeterred, she spent part of her senior year using Lego bricks to build a scale model of a farm. The model served both as her senior thesis and as a job application. Seeing no way out, Lego hired her, in 1984, for a three-week trial period. She has been with the company ever since, and is perhaps the most satisfied worker in the history of employment.

Berger's job is building things out of Lego bricks. Her works include the six-foot-tall red-bearded pirate that stands in the Lego department of F.A.O. Schwarz, on Fifth Avenue, and the six-foot-tall roller coaster, part of an animal amusement park, in the window of the Toys "R" Us in Herald Square. They also include the thirteen-foot-tall (and twenty-seven-and-a-half-foot-wide) replica of the United States Capitol which, along with a number of models of other national landmarks and monuments, recently spent a little more than a month on display at A. & S. Plaza, on West Thirty-third Street. All these models are made entirely of Lego bricks (the Capitol contains more than half a million), and all were assembled by Lego's staff of model-designers and model-builders, of which Berger is the head. The company uses the models as promotions. The Capitol was part of a traveling show that visited ten shopping malls during 1990 and is now in the process of being split up and parcelled out to

Words to Know

undeterred (uhn di TERD) adj.: Not discouraged
promotions (pruh MOH shuhnz) n.: Advertisements

various children's museums. Most people, upon seeing the Capitol model, have two reactions. The first is "Hey, the White House!" The second is "I can't believe somebody built that out of Lego bricks!"

"When we build a model, we don't use any bricks that you can't buy in stores, and we don't alter them or cut them or do anything weird to them," Berger told us not long ago, when we went to visit her in Enfield. "First, the designers draw the model on special graph paper that is scaled to the bricks. Then they build a prototype without gluing it, to prove that it can be done. Then the model-builders make an exact copy and glue it together. They also make sure it's as hollow

as possible, so it will be easier to move around." Some of the moving around is done in two custom-built air-ride semitrailers.

Lego's model-builders work at long tables that can be raised and lowered hydraulically. The tables are connected to an elaborate ventilation system that whisks away fumes from the glue, which is kept in Elmer's bottles but is actually methyl ethyl ketone, a potent solvent that causes the plastic of the bricks to fuse. Once a model has been glued, it can be taken out into the parking lot of a shopping mall, say, and washed down with a garden hose or scrubbed with Formula 409. It can also be left outside for just about as long as you like. The visitors' parking lot at the company headquarters is furnished with an earlier version of the Capitol model, which is kept there year-round.

Francie Berger is thirty years old. She wears aviator glasses and, occasionally, white go-go boots. Her hair is brown and is cut in a long shag. In her office she has a desk, a telephone, a lamp, a photograph of herself chatting with the architect Philip Johnson, some other things, and dozens of bins containing Lego bricks, all sorted by color and type. The Lego building system consists at the moment of roughly thirteen hundred different elements, and Berger is allowed to have as many of any of them as she wants. If she uses up all the pieces in one of her bins, she simply walks into another part of the building and gets more.

Berger's life thus far has been fashioned almost entirely of Lego bricks. When she was married, in 1988, her wedding invitation was decorated with a photograph of a three-foot-tall red Lego hippopotamus bride and groom. Building the hippopotamuses took Berger and her fiancé, a welder, more than two months. On top of the couple's wedding cake was a smaller Lego model, of a human bride and groom. When other Lego employees get married, they often borrow this decoration for their cakes. Each December, Berger and her husband use Lego bricks to build a seasonal tableau beneath their Christmas tree.

Berger does most of her work in her office, but sometimes she travels to shopping malls or state fairs and builds models while people watch. She and a colleague recently built a copy of the Connecticut Capitol at a fair not far from the company's headquarters. The model was eight and a half feet high, ten feet wide, and six feet deep. Building it consumed a hundred and ninety-two person-hours of labor over twelve days. While Berger and her colleague worked, people gathered around to watch and ask questions. Many of the people wanted to know what they would have to do to get a job at Lego. Every year, Berger receives dozens of letters from children, art students, engineers, architects, and others, all wanting to know the same thing. "A lot of kids ask what kind of college courses they should take," Berger told us. "When I write back, I just kind of explain how I got my job. It was a little unorthodox, but it worked for me."

Berger's job didn't exist when she was hired. At that time, all the models used by Lego's American division were made in Denmark and shipped to the United States. To Berger, that seemed nutty. Why not build those models right here in America, and why not let Francie Berger build them? Today, she supervises two other designers and half a dozen full-time model-builders. All these people are, in effect, manifestations of her determination to spend her life doing the thing she likes best.

 **Respond**

What game, sport, or activity could *you* turn into a career? Jot a response in your journal.

David Owen has written articles for various publications ranging from *The New York Times* to *Rolling Stone* and *Reader's Digest* and writes a monthly humor column for *Home* magazine. His article about Francie Berger appeared in *The New Yorker* magazine. He is also the author of several books, including the Princeton Review's *Cracking the SAT* and *My Usual Game: Adventures in Golf.*

Words to Know

prototype (PROH tuh tīp) *n.*: The original model of something

hydraulically (hi DRAW lik lee) *adv.*: Using the power of fluids

manifestations (man uh fes TAY shuhnz) *n.*: Public proof

MAKE MEANING

Explore Your Reading

Look Back (Recall)

1. What does Francie Berger do for a living?
2. How did she get her job?

Think It Over (Interpret)

3. What talents does Francie Berger need to do her job well? What personal qualities did she display in getting it?
4. In what ways is Francie Berger's job more suited to a teenager than to an adult? Explain.

Go Beyond (Apply)

5. What characteristics would you require in *your* "dream job"? Would you be satisfied with a job like Francie Berger's? Why or why not?

Develop Reading and Literary Skills

Analyze Main Idea and Support

As you read "Lego," you looked for the **main idea,** or central point, that the author was expressing. The writer provides **support** for his main idea through facts, examples, and details, such as those describing Francie Berger's early passion for Legos and her campaign to get a job with the company. To identify the main idea, look for a sentence or phrase that sums up the article. Then check to see how the details the author includes contribute to that main idea.

1. Restate the article's main idea in your own words.
2. List three pieces of supporting information from the article. Explain how they support the article's main idea.

Ideas for Writing

Francie Berger created a career out of her own interests. Consider the possibility of doing that for yourself.

Business Letter Imagine a job that you would be uniquely qualified for, based on your personal interests (say, taste tester for your favorite fast-food chain). Prepare a business letter describing and applying for that job. Persuade the employer to give you a job interview.

Sci-Fi Want Ads Think thirty years ahead, and imagine a very different world from yours, with very different career opportunities. Create a "help wanted" page for a newspaper published in the 2020's. Devise employment ads for the future you imagine.

Ideas for Projects

Career Collage With a group, research, plan, and create a collage displaying images of careers you find appealing. Include illustrations or photographs, as well as pieces from résumés, want ads, and office memos. Combine with other groups to make a careers mural for a wall in your classroom. [Art Link]

Mania-festation Create a spectacular "mania-festation" of your favorite hobby or outside interest and bring it to class. For example, sculpt your own head in clay; create a comic strip showing a typical day in your life; videotape yourself doing standup comedy; design and wear a complete set of handmade clothing or jewelry.

How Am I Doing?

Take a moment to answer these questions:
How can I apply my understanding of main idea and support to my other reading?
What have I learned about turning an interest into a career?

How Do I Shape My World?

Think Critically About the Selections

The selections you have read in this section explore the question "How do I shape my world?" With a partner or a small group, complete one of the following activities to show your understanding of the question. You can present your responses orally or in writing.

1. Most of the selections in this section show someone trying to change some part of his or her world. Which effort did you identify with most, and why? What lessons does the selection teach about shaping the world with your own life? **(Synthesize; Draw Conclusions)**

2. The art on this page shows a potter whose medium of expression is clay. What is *your* medium of expression? Describe how you could use that medium to shape your world. **(Make Inferences; Provide Evidence)**

3. Choose two different characters or speakers from the selections in this section. Compare and contrast their efforts to shape their worlds. Which seems more successful to you, and why? **(Compare and Contrast; Evaluate)**

4. What are the pros and cons about trying to shape your world? Develop your answer, drawing on examples from these selections. **(Synthesize; Provide Evidence)**

Projects

Community-Improvement Poster Create a poster about a social, political, or environmental issue that is important to you. Decide on your target audience and the message you want to communicate; then put together the words and images (photographs

Student Art *On the Wheel* Stratton Huggins
Montgomery Bell Academy
Nashville, Tennessee

or drawings) that will make your point most effectively. Display your poster where it will reach the audience you intend. [Art Link]

Design Your World Think about your community or a place you have lived and imagine how you would like to see it evolve in the future. Design your Future Town by drawing a map that shows where different features would be most conveniently located. Include areas for housing, shopping, recreation, education, and government, for example, and any other features you wish. Take advantage of natural geographic features wherever possible. [Social Studies Link]

Myself, My World

In this unit, you've been reading and thinking about these important questions:

- **How Do I Express Myself?**
- **How Do I Relate to Others?**
- **How Do I Shape My World?**

Project Menu

The selections in this unit have helped you see many options for answering these questions. Now it's time for you to create a project of your own that will help you express yourself, relate to others, and shape your world by adding something new to it.

Self-Portrait To show how you express yourself, create a portrait of yourself and your world in art, dance, drama, or music. Videotape your performance, if possible. Share the videotape with members of the class to enable them to evaluate your presentation.

Class Anthology Work with interested classmates to compile, design, and publish a class anthology of student art and writing, focusing on the theme "Ourselves, Our World." Circulate your completed anthology to parents and faculty as well as to other students. Display the book in the class or school library.

Storytelling Festival Organize a storytelling festival for the local world of your community. Encourage people with interesting stories about true or fictional events of the area to participate and, if you can, invite a professional storyteller to appear. Arrange for a public space for the event, and plan to videotape the festival to archive in your school or local library.

From Questions to Careers

Answering the questions in this unit may help you discover some new career possibilities for yourself. For example, Francie Berger, head designer of Lego models, has built job satisfaction out of a lifelong passion for creating imaginative structures with tiny plastic bricks. Her answer to the question "How Do I Shape My World?" would be simple: "From Legos!" She explains, "A lot of kids ask what kind of college courses they should take" to get a job like hers. "When I write back, I just kind of explain how I got my job. It was a little unorthodox, but it worked for me." (See the selection "Lego" by David Owen.)

What will work for you? Look at some of the careers that may help shape your world in the next few years.

Myself, My World

"I love building things."
WANTED
Civil engineer
Construction worker
Architect
Woodworker

"I'm great with colors."
WANTED
Virtual-reality artist
Fireworks designer
Cartoonist
Interior decorator

"I enjoy giving parties."
WANTED
Restaurant manager
Personnel director
Theme-park planner
Caterer

"I love to pretend."
WANTED
Inventor
Artist
Screenwriter
Actor

Career Day Shape your world by planning, organizing, and executing a career day at your school. Create displays with information about careers that are likely to appeal to students. Invite speakers who have pursued interesting career paths to address the student body in an assembly program. Prepare a report evaluating the program.

Home Town Celebration Invite local leaders to speak to the students in your school about your home town. Designate a theme for this celebration, such as reflections on the history and geographic location of your town. Plan and publicize a program of speakers and arrange to present the speeches in the school auditorium. Write a review of the program for your school or local newspaper. [Social Studies Link]

School of the Future To envision your world of the future, design a school of the future, including subjects, technology and library facilities, and building blueprints and models. Present your design as a proposal to a School Board of the Future.

Guided Writing

Firsthand Biography

What is a firsthand biography?

Who have been the most important people in your life? There are probably many individuals who have played special roles in your life and influenced your understanding of both yourself and the world around you. These might include relatives, friends, teachers, or other adults you admire. Each person most likely has had distinctive features and qualities that make him or her memorable to you.

Guidelines • • • • • • • • • • • • • • • • • • •

In writing a firsthand biography, you

- *describe an important person in your life.*

- *provide details that give readers a clear picture of the person's outstanding traits.*

- *express your thoughts and feelings about the person, including why he or she is important to you.*

Prewriting _____

How can I decide on a person and choose details to use?

Make a list. Brainstorm to think of several individuals who have had a special effect on your life. Make a list of these people and then circle the name of the person who stands out most in your mind.

Use a cluster diagram. You need to make sure you will have enough details to describe your subject clearly. Write the name of the person on a sheet of paper and cluster around it words and phrases that capture significant characteristics of the person.

Use several categories of details in the cluster. Choose features that make your subject different from other people.

Cluster Diagram

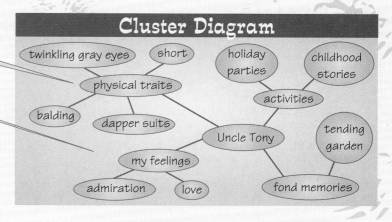

twinkling gray eyes

short

holiday parties

childhood stories

physical traits

activities

balding

dapper suits

Uncle Tony

tending garden

my feelings

admiration

love

fond memories

Look through your store-house of memories. Find journal entries, letters, cards, photographs, notes, or other items that relate to the person you've chosen. Record important details and thoughts these items trigger in your mind.

Interview the person. If possible, arrange to meet with the person you're writing about to gather more information. First prepare a list of questions to ask during the interview. You might ask the person about his or her background, beliefs, or most memorable experiences.

Interview Questions

What are your earliest memories?
What have been the most important events in your life?
How would you describe yourself?
What are your most important values in life?

Drafting

What steps should I follow when I start writing?

Begin by catching your reader's interest. Start with a quotation, a dramatic moment, or a vivid detail that will make your audience want to read more about the person you're describing.

Focus on the most outstanding features. Include only the most important details that will help you bring the person to life for your readers, for example, significant actions, dialogue, and sensory details. Choose details that create a main impression, or central feeling, about your subject. Avoid using unnecessary details or information that doesn't add to the main impression.

Writing Model

Since I never knew any of my grandparents, my Great-Great-Uncle Tony became the best grandfather I could have hoped for.

Include specific incidents. Make sure readers will understand why your subject is important to you. Describe or suggest your thoughts and feelings about the person, for example, his or her personality, behavior, attitudes, or relationships with people.

Revising and Editing

How can I improve my firsthand biography?

Is it clear why you chose this person? Besides describing features and qualities of your subject, make sure you have conveyed why he or she has made a significant impact on your life. Ask yourself whether readers will understand why the person is so memorable to you.

Writing Model

Since I never knew any of my grandparents, my Great-Great-Uncle Tony became the best grandfather I could have hoped for. I will never forget his kindness, sense of humor, generosity, and lively spirit.

The writer added a sentence to tell why the person is important in his life.

Work with a writing partner.

Read and evaluate each other's writing to discuss improvements you each might make. Use the following kinds of revision questions with your partner.

Prepare and proofread a final draft.

Check your writing for errors in grammar, usage, and punctuation, and make any necessary corrections. Remember that mechanical mistakes distract readers from appreciating the subject of your writing.

Computer Tip

Use the spell-check feature to help you find and correct spelling mistakes.

Checkpoints for Revision • • • • • • • •

- *How can I make my beginning capture readers' interest more strongly?*
- *How can I focus better on the most significant features of the person?*
- *What details about the person's appearance, actions, or personality do I need to add to help bring him or her to life more vividly?*
- *What unnecessary information can I eliminate?*
- *How can I make the person's importance in my life more clear for readers?*

Checkpoints for Editing • • • • • • • • •

- *Have I used pronouns correctly?*
- *Did I use appositives to make my writing economical?*

For practice in these skills, see the **Develop Your Style** lessons on the next two pages.

Publishing and Presenting

In what ways can I share my firsthand biography sketch?

✔ Send a copy of your writing to the person you chose as your subject.

✔ Read your sketch to members of your household.

✔ With classmates, gather your sketches into a classroom anthology called *People Profiles*.

✔ Enter your work in a local or national writing contest.

How Did I Do?

What have I learned about my writing process from this assignment?

- *Did taking time to revise help me find ways to focus on the most important details in my writing? How can I use what I learned for future writing assignments?*

- *Did writing about the person deepen or change my understanding of him or her, or of myself? If so, how?*

Develop Your Style

1 Use Pronouns Correctly

How do I know which pronoun to use?

Ask yourself whether you need a subject pronoun or an object pronoun. In writing a firsthand biography you use lots of pronouns. It's important to note the kind of pronoun to use in a sentence.

Use subject pronouns when the pronoun is the subject of a verb or follows a linking verb. The subject pronouns are:

I	he	she	it
we	you	they	

Use object pronouns when the pronoun is a direct or indirect object of a verb or the object of a preposition. The object pronouns are:

me	him	her	it
us	them	you	

Practice using correct pronouns. Choose the correct pronoun in each of these sentences. Tell why you used the pronoun you chose.

1. Uncle Tony gave (I/me) a quarter every week.

2. His sense of humor always impressed (I/me).

3. Uncle Tony and I both like to dance, but I am a better dancer than (he/him).

4. My uncle shared his favorite stories with (we/us).

Check the pronouns in your firsthand biography. Perhaps you find a sentence like this one.

> No one could have been a better influence on me than him.

Mentally finish the end of the sentence to see what the correct pronoun choice would be:

> No one could have been a better influence on me than (he/him) was.

Revise to use a subject pronoun here. The pronoun *he* is the correct choice.

> No one could have been a better influence on me than *he*.

This sentence uses a pronoun as the subject.

Writing Model

I love my Uncle Tony. The most respected member of my family was he.

This sentence uses a subject pronoun following the linking verb *was*.

This pronoun is the direct object of the verb *amazed*.

Writing Model

Uncle Tony's garden amazed me.

Uncle Tony gave me vegetables from his garden.

My favorite stories all came from him.

This pronoun is the indirect object of the verb *gave*.

This pronoun is the object of the preposition *from*.

2 Use Appositives for Economy

How can I streamline my writing?

Use appositives to combine two sentences into one. An **appositive** is a noun or phrase placed after another noun or pronoun to help explain it:

> Uncle Tony, *my great-uncle on my father's side,* was my favorite relative.

Using appositives to combine sentences economizes on the number of words you need to use. Varying your sentences with appositives will also make your writing more interesting.

Writing Models

All that's really needed from the second sentence is the phrase *substitute grandfather.* Using that phrase as an appositive creates one sentence that is more economical than the other two.

Great-uncle Tony was kind and generous.
He was my substitute grandfather.

Great-uncle Tony, *my substitute grandfather,* was kind and generous.

Each turtle had a name. One was called Racing Rick.

Each turtle had a name, *like Racing Rick.*

Using the appositive gets the same information across economically and avoids the choppiness of two similar short sentences.

Practice using appositives. Revise these sentences to include appositives.

1. Although my grandfather died many years ago, my grandmother is still alive. Her name is Sadie.
2. Sadie was born in Russia. She was the oldest of five girls.
3. Sadie is eighty years old. We call Sadie our "forever-young granny."
4. She embodies the lively spirit of the Russian people. She is still singing and dancing and telling great humorous stories, too.

Look at your firsthand biography for places to use appositives. As you revise a first draft, look for chances to combine two sentences using an appositive. You'll be able to present information more quickly and make your writing flow more smoothly at the same time.

Book News

Featured Review

Flowers for Algernon
by Daniel Keyes

This story is told by Charlie Gordon, who is chosen, along with a white rat named Algernon, to be the subject of a scientific experiment. Born with a subnormal IQ, Charlie undergoes an operation and treatment to increase his intelligence. The experiment is a success and Charlie is transformed into a super genius.

The novel follows Charlie's progress from a likeable but barely literate man to a person capable of

highly technical scientific research. The subjects of his research are the white rat, Algernon, and himself. When the white rat begins to show signs that the experiment is failing, Charlie guesses what his fate will be also. He knows he has experienced the full extent of his capabilities and now has to learn how to live with the limitations that are to follow.

Introducing the Author

Daniel Keyes wrote *Flowers for Algernon* as a short story for a magazine. His story won the Hugo award (1959) for the best science novelette. The story was made into a television drama and then enlarged into this novel. The novel was the

basis for the motion picture *Charly*.

Keyes was born in Brooklyn, New York, and received his Bachelor's and Master's degrees from Brooklyn College. In addition to his work as a writer he has been a merchant seaman, a ship's purser, a high school teacher and college professor, and a fiction editor.

Pass It On: Student Choices

Children of the River
by Linda Crew

Reviewed by Tessa Swan, Pacheco Elementary School, Redding, California

This book was really different from most other stories that I read. It was interesting and never boring. The character, Sundara, showed me how difficult it is to choose between the ways of your culture and your friendships with others. I also learned how much people will sacrifice just to come to the United States. If there is a sequel to this book, I want to read it, too!

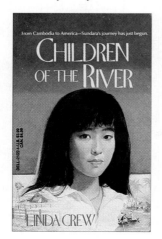

Journal

MY WORLD • • • • • • • • • •

When the Legends Die
by Hal Borland

Reviewed by Jared Mercier, Marshfield Junior High School, Marshfield, Wisconsin

This book is especially interesting for showing the Native American experience. The main character, Thomas Black Bull, is a Native American who finds he has to discover his identity in order to keep others from taking it away from him. I could especially relate to the situation where kids are treating him badly and other people are telling him that they're really trying to be his friends! I recommend reading this book to learn how Thomas discovers what is important about himself.

Dogsong
by Gary Paulsen

Reviewed by Beau Brooks, Cresthill Middle School, Highland Ranch, Colorado

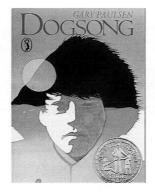

Gary Pauslen's book is filled with excitement and adventure. Set in Alaska, the story tells about Russel's strength, will, and courage in running his sled dogs 1,400 miles over the ice, tundra, and mountains. His story showed how important it is to learn who you are. I admired him especially for standing up for what he strongly believed in.

Read On: More Choices

Izzy, Willy Nilly
by Cynthia Voigt

White Hare's Horses
by Penina Keen Spinka

Lives of the Musicians: Good Times, Bad Times (And What the Neighbors Thought)
by Kathleen Krull

Five Women Photographers
by Sylvia Wolf

Share the Fun

Book Art Display Present your response to the book you read in the form of a graphic design or media presentation. Display your art along with an explanation of the connection between the book and the art.

Audiotape Reviews Record your review of a book on audiotape. Exchange your tape with others who have read the book and add their reviews to the audiotape. File the audiotapes by book title and make them available to the class.

Panel Discussion Present a panel discussion of a book. Organize the presentation so that each panel member presents a different aspect of the book. Invite questions from your audience following the presentation.

On the Internet Look for discussions of the book you read on the Internet. Form a chat group with others who have read the book. Report the responses from others and compare them to yours. Share the responses with the class.

GLOSSARY

Pronunciation Key

The vocabulary and footnotes in this textbook are respelled to aid pronunciation. A syllable in CAPITAL LETTERS receives the most stress. The key below lists the letters used for respelling. It includes examples of words using each sound and shows how the words would be respelled.

Symbol	Example	Respelled	Symbol	Example	Respelled
a	hat, cat	hat, cat	oh	no, toe	noh, toh
ay	pay, ape	pay, ayp	oo	look, pull, put	look, pool, poot
ah	hot, stop	haht, stahp	oy	boil, toy	boyl, toy
aw	law, all, horn	law, awl, hawrn	oo	ooze, tool, crew	ooz, tool, croo
			ow	plow, out	plow, owt
e	met, elf, ten	met, elf, ten			
ee	bee, eat, flea	bee, eet, flee	u	up, cut, flood	up, cut, flud
er	learn, sir, fur	lern, ser, fer	yoo	few, use	fyoo, yooz
i	is	fit	uh	a in ago	uh GO
ī	mile, sigh	mīle sīgh		e in agent	AY juhnt
				i in sanity	SAN uh tee
				o in compress	kuhm PRES
				u in focus	FOH kuhs

A

aghast (uh GAST) *adj.*: Horrified

allegiance (uh LEE juhns) *n.*: Loyalty

amor (ah MOR) *n.*: Spanish for *love*

apprenticeship (a PREN tis ship) *n.*: The time spent by a person working for a master craftsman in a craft or trade in return for instruction and, formerly, support

aptitude (AP tuh tood) *n.*: Inborn skill

audible (AW duh buhl) *adv.*: Able to be heard

B

badgering (BAJ er ing) *v.*: Tormenting

baling hook (BAY ling HOOK) *n.*: Large hooks used for lifting heavy bundles

barracuda (ba ruh KOO duh) *n.*: A very fierce fish

batter (BAT er) *v.*: Hit over and over

bolo tie (BOH loh TĪ) *n.*: A man's string tie, held together with a decorated sliding device

bravado (bruh VAH doh) *n.*: A show of pretended courage

brooch (BROHCH) *n.*: Large ornamental pin

butte (BYOOT) *n.*: A steep hill rising up from a flat plain

C

cartographer (kar TAHG ruh fer) *n.*: A mapmaker

cease (SEES) *v.*: Stop

colleries (KOL yur ees) *n.*: Coal mines

conspicuous (kuhn SPIK yoo uhs) *adj.*: Easy to notice

constellation (kahn stuh LAY shuhn) *n.*: A cluster of stars

contemptuously (kuhn TEMP choo uhs lee) *adv.*: Scornfully

contend (kuhn TEND) *v.*: Struggle; fight

countenance (KOWN tuh nuhns) *n.*: Face

credibility (kred uh BIL i tee) *n.*: Believability

crown (KROWN) *n.*: The red comb on top of the rooster's head

cub (KUHB) *n.*: Beginner

D

defiant (di FĪ uhnt) *adj.*: Openly rebellious

derisively (di RĪ siv lee) *adv.*: Ridiculing

dismissal (dis MIS uhl) *n.*: Sending someone away

dusk (DUHSK) *n.*: Time just after sunset before nightfall

dwindle (DWIN duhl) *v.*: Lessen

E

ecstatically (ek STAT ihk lee) *adv.*: Joyfully

etched (ECHT) *adj.*: Drawn or engraved

F

façade (fuh SAHD) *n.*: Front of a building

fanatic (fuh NAT ik) *n.*: One who is overly enthusiastic about something

fatigue (fuh TEEG) *n.*: Great weariness

flex (FLEKS) *v.*: Bend and contract, as with a muscle

furtive (FUR tiv) *adj.*: Sneaky

futility (fyoo TIL uh tee) *n.*: Sense of hopelessness

G

gaunt (GAWNT) *adj.*: Extremely thin

georgette (jor JET) *n.*: A thin silk cloth

glint (GLINT) *v.*: Flash

glockenspiel (GLOK uhn speel) *n.*: Musical instrument with flat metal bars that makes bell-like tones when struck

gratifying (GRAHT i fī ing) *n.*: Giving pleasure or satisfaction

grovel (GRUHV uhl) *v.*: Behave very humbly

H

hydraulically (hi DRAW lik lee) *adv.*: Using the power of fluids

I

impeccably (im PEK uh blee) *adv.*: Flawlessly

imperative (im PER uh tihv) *adj.*: Absolutely necessary

incredulous (in KREJ oo luhs) *adj.*: Not believing

indicative (in DIK uh tiv) *adj.*: Giving a suggestion; showing

inquest (IN kwest) *n.*: Investigation in a court of law

intimation (in tuh MAY shuhn) *n.*: A hint

J

jibara (HEE bah ruh) *n.*: Spanish for *poor farmer*

judicious (joo DI shuhs) *adj.*: Careful

L

lead (LEED) *n.*: Weight that is lowered to test the depth of a river

listlessly (LIST lis lee) *adv.*: Wearily; without energy

luna (LOO nah) *n.*: Spanish for *moon*

luster (LUHS ter) *n.*: Glow

M

maestro (MĪS troh) *n.*: A master in any art, especially a great composer, conductor, or teacher of music

manifestation (man uh fes TAY shuhn) *n.*: Public proof

Mason (MAY sun) **jar** *n.*: A glass jar with a wide mouth and screw top, used for canning and preserving

meanly (MEEN lee) *adv.*: Unkindly

mesmerize (MEZ muh rīz) *adj.*: Almost hypnotize

moccasin (MOK uh sin) *n.*: Heelless slipper of soft flexible leather, originally worn by Native Americans

monotone (MAHN uh tohn) *n.*: A single color; a flat, unvaried sound

mote (MOHT) *n.*: A speck of dust or other tiny particle

N

noggin (NAHG in) *n.*: Slang for head or brain

O

orator (OR uh ter) *n.*: Person who make public speeches

P

pantomime (PAN toh mīm) *n.*: A performance without words

periscope (PER uh skohp) *n.*: An instrument containing mirrors and lenses to see objects not in a direct line from the viewer; often used in submarines to see objects above the water

perseverance (per suh VEER uhns) *n.*: Steady determination

pneumonia (noo MOHN yuh) *n.*: A serious infection of the lungs

podium (POH dee uhm) *n.*: A low platform for a conductor

pomme blanche (pum BLAHNSH) *n.*: French for "white apple," the fruit of the breadroot plant in the western U.S.

prairie (PRAYR ee) *n.*: Large area of level grassland

prance (PRANS) *v.*: Hop around

pretext (PRE tekst) *n.*: Excuse

procession (proh SESH uhn) *n.*: A long line of people walking

prodigy (PRAHD uh jee) *n.*: A wonder; an unusually talented person

promotion (pruh MOH shuhn) *n.*: Advertisement

prototype (PROH tuh tip) *n.*: The original model of something

psyching (SĪ king) *v.*: Slang for playing on a person's mental state

purify (PYOR uh fī) *v.*: Get rid of polluting matter

R

radiant (RAY dee uhnt) *adj.*: Shining brightly

reinforced (ree in FORST) *adj.*: Strengthened

remnant (REM nunt) *n.*: Leftover part

reputation (rep yoo TAY shuhn) *n.*: What other people think about someone

resonant (RES uh nuhnt) *adj.*: Vibrating with sound

S

sage (SAYJ) *n.*: A grayish-green herb of the mint family, sometimes believed to have healing powers

saunter (SAWN ter) *v.*: Walk slowly

scold (SKOHLD) *v.*: Criticize in a harsh way

shuffling (SHUHF ling) *n.*: A slightly dragging walk

sierra (see AYR uh) *n.*: Mountain range

Sioux (SOO) *n.*: Native American tribes of the northern plains of the United States and nearby southern Canada

skulk (SKUHLK) *v.*: Sneak

snare (SNAYR) *v.*: Capture

stolidly (STAHL id lee) *adv.*: Unemotionally

strain (STRAYN) *n.*: Bit of music

stupefy (STOO puh fī) *v.*: Stun

sumac (SOO mak) *n.*: A treelike plant with pointed leaves

surplus (SER pluhs) *n.*: More than enough; extra

syllable (SIL uh buhl) *n.*: One of the parts into which a word is divided

T

tendon (TEN duhn) *n.*: Tough body tissue that connects the muscles to the bones

tepee (TEE pee) *n.*: A cone-shaped tent of animal skins, used by the Plains Indians

terrain (te RAYN) *n.*: An area of land

texas-tender (TEKS es TEN der) *n.*: The waiter in the officers' quarters. On Mississippi steamboats, rooms were named after the states. The officers' area, which was the largest, was named after what was then the largest state, Texas

thong (THONG) *n.*: A narrow strip of leather

topographer (tuh PAHG ruh fer) *n.*: A person who makes maps showing the surface features of a place

tranquil (TRAN kwil) *adj.*: Calm; peaceful

transform (trans FORM) *v.*: Completely change

U

undaunted (uhn DAWN ted) *adj.*: Not frightened

undeterred (uhn di TERD) *adj.*: Not discouraged

unmentionable (un MEN shun uh buhl) *adj.*: Not fit for polite conversation

unnerving (un NERV ing) *adj.*: Upsetting

V

valedictorian (val uh dik TOR ee uhn) *n.*: The highest ranking student in a class

ventriloquist (ven TRIL uh kwist) *n.*: Someone who speaks through a puppet or dummy

vexing (VECK sing) *adj.*: Troubling

vision quest (VIZH en KWEST) *n.*: A search for a revelation that would aid understanding

vituperation (vī too pe RAY shuhn) *n.*: Abusive language

vocational (voh CAY shuhn uhl) *adj.*: Aimed at teaching a trade rather than preparing for college

W

wainscoting (WAYN skaht ing) *n.*: Paneled wood trim

whelp (WHELP) *n.*: A young dog or puppy; slang for a disrespectful young person

Index of Fine Art

Index of Authors and Titles

Page numbers in italics refer to biographical information.

Index of Skills

Literary Terms
Character, K25, K42
Character Behavior, K14, K27, K80
    Analyze, K14
    Examine, K80
    Predict, K27
Character's Motivation, K72, K79
    Recognize, K72
    Understand, K79
Character's Problems and Solutions, K20
Compare and Contrast, K41, K87, K129
Comparisons in Poetry, K94
Conflict, K40, K42, K44, K51, K100
    Analyze in Drama, K40
    Analyze in Plot, K51
    Identify Conflict, K44, K100
Conflict Between Characters, K109
Drama, K40
    Analyze Conflict in, K40
Draw Conclusions, K87, K129
Evaluate, K129
First-Person Narrator, K60
Ideas in Poems, K110
Indirect Characterization, K86
Lyric Poetry, K71
Main Idea and Support, K124, K128
    Analyze, K128
    Read for, K124
Make Inferences, K41, K87, K129
Make Judgments, K41
Metaphor, K88, K98
    Understand Simile and Metaphor, K98
Mood, K88, K90
    Identify a Mood, K90
    Mood in Poetry, K93
Narrator's Viewpoint, K52, K114, K123
    Analyze, K114
    Make Judgments About, K123
    Observe, K52
Plot, K42, K51, K65
    Analyze Conflict in, K51
    Infer Theme From Actions, K65
Poetry, K19, K88, K93, K113
    Looking at, K88
    Mood in, K93
    Understand Speakers in, K19
    Understand Themes in, K113
Relationships, K66
Setting, K42
Short Story, K42
    Looking at, K42
Simile, K88, K98
    Understand Simile and Metaphor, K98
Speakers, K16
Speakers in Poetry, K19
Theme, K42, K65
    Infer Theme From Actions, K65
Themes in Poems, K113

Reading and Thinking Skills
Analyze, K14, K40, K51, K86, K93, K109, K110
  K114, K128
    Narrator's Viewpoint, K114
    Character Behavior, K14

Conflict Between Characters, K109
Conflict in Drama, K40
Conflict in Plot, K51
Ideas in Poems, K110
Indirect Characterization, K86
Main Idea and Support, K128
Mood in Poetry, K93
Background, K4
Comparisons, K94
    Identify Comparisons in Poetry, K94
Connect, K3
Follow up, K13
Infer Theme From Actions, K65
Main Idea and Support, K124
Make Inferences, K62
Make Judgments, K123
    About the Narrator, K123
Observe, K11, K52
    Narrator's Viewpoint, K52
Predict, K3
    Character's Behavior, K27
Preview, K2
Problems and Solutions, K20
Provide Evidence, K41, K87, K129
Questions, K3
Read for Main Idea and Support, K124
Respond, K3
Synthesize, K41, K87, K129
Visualize, K3

Ideas for Writing
Analysis of Conflict, K51
Another Point of View, K25
Biographical Essay, K113
Book Jacket, K113
Business Letter, K128
Cause and Effect Essay, K86
Character Description, K71
Comparison-Contrast Essay, K19
Describe a Mood, K93
Evaluate a Figure of Speech, K98
Evaluate Competition, K60
Evaluation, K14
Feature Article, K123
Firsthand Biography, K25, K65
Firsthand Biography (Guided Writing Lesson),
  K132
Letter From a Character, K79
Letter to the Future, K79
Letters, K86
Mood Poems, K93
Narration and Dialogue, K109
New Viewpoint, K14
Original Folk Tale, K65
Personal Letter, K40
Persuasive Essay, K123
Persuasive Letter, K109
Play Review, K40
Poem About You, K19
Poem, K98
Poetic Tribute, K71
Research Report, K79
Sci-Fi Want Ads, K128
Story Retelling, K60

What-If Story, K51

Ideas for Projects
Advertisement, K98
Art Appreciation, K93
Audio or Video Recording, K19
Career Collage, K128
Career Day, K1
Career Resource Book, K123
Career Road Map, K123
Class Anthology, K1
Collage, K19
Collage of Influences, K87
Communication Bulletin Board, K25
Community Cleanup, K14
Community Improvement Poster, K129
Cookbook, K71
Debate, K40
Depression Documentary, K86
Design Your World, K129
Fame Gallery, K113
Fan Club, K113
Folk Tale Collection, K65
Hometown Celebration, K1
Mania-festation, K128
Mark Twain Day, K109
Music Video, K40
Oral Report, K109, K60
Panel Discussion, K60
Poetic Music Video, K41
Portrait of a Life, K87
Poster Display, K51
Recording, K51
Recordings, K93
Relationship Design, K14
Research Presentation, K79
Research Report, K25, K98
Research, K71
Research: Graph, K86
School of the Future, K1
Self-Portrait, K1
Storyboard Timeline, K41
Storytelling Festival, K1
Taped Interview, K79
Wall Collage, K65

Student Review Board

Acharya, Arundhathi
Cecelia Snyder Middle School
Bensalem, Pennsylvania

Adkisson, Grant
McClintock Middle School
Charlotte, North Carolina

Akuna, Kimberly
Harriet Eddy Middle School
Elk Grove, California

Amdur, Samantha
Morgan Selvidge Middle School
Ballwin, Missouri

Arcilla, Richard
Village School
Closter, New Jersey

Arredondo, Marcus
Keystone School
San Antonio, Texas

Auten, Kristen
Bernardo Heights Middle School
San Diego, California

Backs, Jamie
Cross Keys Middle School
Florissant, Missouri

Baldwin, Katie
Bonham Middle School
Temple, Texas

Barber, Joanna
Chenery School
Belmont, Massachusetts

Bates, Maureen
Chestnut Ridge Middle School
Sewell, New Jersey

Bates, Meghan
Chestnut Ridge Middle School
Sewell, New Jersey

Beber, Nick
Summit Middle School
Dillon, Colorado

Becker, Jason
Hicksville Middle School
Hicksville, New York

Belfon, Loreal
Highland Oaks Middle School
Miami, Florida

Belknap, Jessica
Hughes Middle School
Long Beach, California

Bennet, Joseph
Conner Middle School
Hebron, Kentucky

Birke, Lori
LaSalle Springs Middle School
Glencoe, Missouri

Bleichrodt, Angela
Beulah School
Beulah, Colorado

Block, Kyle
Hall-McCarter Middle School
Blue Springs, Missouri

Brendecke, Sarah Grant
Baseline Middle School
Boulder, Colorado

Brooks, Beau
Cresthill Middle School
Highlands Ranch, Colorado

Bruder, Jennifer
Nipher Middle School
Kirkwood, Missouri

Brunsfeld, Courtney
Moscow Junior High School
Moscow, Idaho

Burnett, Joseph
Markham Intermediate School
Placerville, California

Burrows, Tammy
Meadowbrook Middle School
Orlando, Florida

Calles, Miguel
Lennox Middle School
Lennox, California

Casanova, Christina
McKinley Classic Junior Academy
St. Louis, Missouri

Ceaser, Cerena
Templeton Middle School
Templeton, California

Chapman, Jon
Black Butte Middle School
Shingletown, California

Cho, Hwa
Miami Lakes Middle School
Miami Lakes, Florida

Chu, Rita
Orange Grove Middle School
Hacienda Heights, California

Church, John
Nathan Hale Middle School
Norwalk, Conneticut

Clouse, Melissa Ann
Happy Valley Elementary School
Anderson, California

Colbert, Ryanne
William H. Crocker School
Hillsborough, California

Crucet, Jennine
Miami Lakes Middle School
Miami Lakes, Florida

Culp, Heidi
Eastern Christian Middle School
Wyckoff, New Jersey

Cummings, Amber
Pacheco Elementary School
Redding, California

Curran, Christopher
Cresthill Middle School
Highlands Ranch, Colorado

D'Angelo, Samantha
Cresthill Middle School
Highlands Ranch, Colorado

D'Auria, Jeffrey
Nyack Middle School
Nyack, New York

D'Auria, Katherine
Upper Nyack Elementary School
Upper Nyack, New York

D'Auria, Patrick
Nyack Middle School
Nyack, New York

Daughtride, Katharyne
Lakeview Middle School
Winter Garden, Florida

Donato, Bridget
Felix Festa Junior High School
New City, New York

Donato, Christopher
Felix Festa Junior High School
New City, New York

Dress, Brian
Hall-McCarter Middle School
Blue Springs, Missouri

Drilling, Sarah
Milford Junior High School
Milford, Ohio

Fernandez, Adrian
Shenandoah Middle School
Coral Gables, Florida

Flores, Amanda
Orange Grove Middle School
Hacienda Heights, California

Flynn, Patricia
Camp Creek Middle School
College Park, Georgia

Ford, Adam
Cresthill Middle School
Highlands Ranch, Colorado

Fowler, Sabrina
Camp Creek Middle School
College Park, Georgia

Fox, Anna
Georgetown School
Georgetown, California

Freeman, Ledon
Atlanta, Georgia

Frid-Nielsen, Snorre
Branciforte Elementary School
Santa Cruz, California

Frosh, Nicole
Columbia Middle School
Aurora, Colorado

Gerretson, Bryan
Marshfield Junior High School
Marshfield, Wisconsin

Gillis, Shalon Michelle
Wagner Middle School
Philadelphia, Pennsylvania

Gonzales, Michael
Kitty Hawk Junior High School
Universal City, Texas

Goodman, Andrew
Richmond School
Hanover, New Hampshire

Granberry, Kemoria
Riviera Middle School
Miami, Florida

Groppe, Karissa
McCormic Junior High School
Cheyenne, Wyoming

Hadley, Michelle
Hopkinton Middle School
Hopkinton, Massachusetts

Hall, Katie
C.R. Anderson Middle School
Helena, Montana

Hamilton, Tim
Columbia School
Redding, California

Hawkins, Arie
East Norriton Middle School
Norristown, Pennsylvania

Hawkins, Jerry
Carrollton Junior High School
Carrollton, Missouri

Hayes, Bridget
Point Fermin Elementary School
San Pedro, California

Heinen, Jonathan
Broomfield Heights Middle School
Broomfield, Colorado

Hibbard, Erin
Willard Grade Center
Ada, Oklahoma

Hinners, Katie
Spaulding Middle School
Loveland, Ohio

Houston, Robert
Allamuchy Township Elementary
Allamuchy, New Jersey

Huang, Kane
Selridge Middle School
Ballwin, Missouri

Hudson, Vanessa
Bates Academy
Detroit, Michigan

Hutchison, Erika
C.R. Anderson Middle School
Helena, Montana

Hykes, Melissa
Meadowbrook Middle School
Orlando, Florida

Jackson, Sarah Jane
Needles Middle School
Needles, California

Jigarjian, Kathryn
Weston Middle School
Weston, Massachusetts

Johnson, Becky
Wheatland Junior High School
Wheatland, Wyoming

Johnson, Bonnie
West Middle School
Colorado Springs, Colorado

Johnson, Courtney
Oak Run Elementary School
Oak Run, California

Jones, Mary Clara
Beulah Middle School
Beulah, Colorado

Jones, Neil
Central School
Chillicothe, Missouri

Juarez, Sandra
Adams City Middle School
Thornton, Colorado

Juarez, Karen
Rincon Middle School
Escondito, California

Karas, Eleni
Our Lady of Grace
Encino, California

King, Autumn
Roberts Paideia Academy
Cincinnati, Ohio

Kossenko, Anna
Plantation Middle School
Plantation, Florida

Kurtz, Rachel
Paul Revere Middle School
Los Angeles, California

Lambino, Victoria
Henry H. Wells Middle School
Brewster, New York

Lamour, Katleen
Highland Oaks Middle School
North Miami Beach, Florida

Larson, Veronica
McClintock Middle School
Charlotte, North Carolina

Liao, Wei-Cheng
Nobel Middle School
Northridge, California

Lightfoot, Michael
Mission Hill Middle School
Santa Cruz, California

Lippman, Andrew
Thomas A. Blake Middle School
Medfield, Massachusetts

Lo, Melissa
Lincoln Middle School
Santa Monica, California

Lopez, Eric
Irvine Intermediate School
Costa Mesa, California

Lowery, Ry-Yon
East Norriton Middle School
Norristown, Pennsylvania

Macias, Edgar
Teresa Hughes Elementary School
Cudahy, California

Madero, Vanessa
Mathew J. Brletic Elementary
Parlier, California

Mandel, Lily
Mission Hill Junior High School
Santa Cruz, California

Manzano, Elizabeth Josephine
Hillside Elementary School
San Bernardino, California

Marentes, Crystal-Rose
Orange Grove Middle School
Hacienda Heights, California

Martinez, Desiree
Wheatland Junior High School
Wheatland, Wyoming

Massey, Drew
Union 6th and 7th Grade Center
Tulsa, Oklahoma

Matson, Josh
Canyon View Junior High School
Orem, Utah

Maxcy, Donald, Jr.
Camp Creek Middle School
Atlanta, Georgia

Maybruch, Robyn
Middle School 141
Riverdale, New York

Mayer, Judith
Burlingame Intermediate School
Burlingame, California

McCarter, Jennifer
Washburn School
Cincinnati, Ohio

McCarthy, Megan
Richmond School
Hanover, New Hampshire

McCombs, Juanetta
Washburn School
Cincinnati, Ohio

McGann, Kristen
Orange Grove Middle School
Hacienda Heights, California

McKelvey, Steven
Providence Christian Academy
Atlanta, Georgia

McQuary, Megan
CCA Baldi Middle School
Philadelphia, Pennsylvania

Mercier, Jared
Marshfield Junior High School
Marshfield, Wisconsin

Merrill, Nick
Windham Middle School
Windham, Maine

Miller, Catherine
Neil Armstrong Junior High School
Levittown, Pennsylvania

Miller, Kristen
Marina Village Junior High
El Dorado Hills, California

Montgomery, Tyler
North Cow Creek School
Palo Cedro, California

Mueller, Jessica
Spaulding Middle School
Loveland, Ohio

Mueler, John
St. Catherine School
Milwaukee, Wisconsin

Mulligan, Rebecca
Herbert Hoover Middle School
Oklahoma City, Oklahoma

Murgel, John
Beulah School
Beulah, Colorado

Murphy, Mathew
St. Wenceslaus School
Omaha, Nebraska

Neeley, Alex
Allamuchy Township School
Allamuchy, New Jersey

Nelsen-Smith, Nicole Marie
Branciforte Elementary
Santa Cruz, California

Ogle, Sarah
Redlands Middle School
Grand Junction, Colorado

Ozeryansky, Svetlana
C.C.A. Baldi Middle School
Philadelphia, Pennsylvania

Pacheco, Vicky
East Whittier Middle School
Whittier, California

Paddack, Geoffrey
Ada Junior High School
Ada, Oklahoma

Palombi, Stephanie
Marina Village Middle School
Cameron Park, California

Panion, Stephanie
Pitts Middle School
Pueblo, Colorado

Parks, Danny
West Cottonwood Junior High School
Cottonwood, California

Parriot, Cassandra
Orange Grove Middle School
Hacienda Heights, California

Paulson, Christina
Jefferson Middle School
Rocky Ford, Colorado

Perez, Iscura
Charles Drew Middle School
Los Angeles, California

Pratt, Lisa
Nottingham Middle Community Education Center
St. Louis, Missouri

Raggio, Jeremiah
Eagleview Middle School
Colorado Springs, Colorado

Raines, Angela
McKinley Classical Academy
St. Louis, Missouri

Ramadan, Mohammad
Ada Junior High School
Ada, Oklahoma

Ramiro, Leah
Magruder Middle School
Torrance, California

Raymond, Elizabeth
Julie A. Traphagen School
Waldwick, New Jersey

Recinos, Julie
Riviera Middle School
Miami, Florida

Reese, Andrea
Moscow Junior High
Moscow, Idaho

Reiners, Andrew
Redlands Middle School
Grand Junction, Colorado

Riddle, Katy
Willard Elementary School
Ada, Okalhoma

Rippe, Chris
La Mesa Junior High School
Santa Clarita, California

Robinson, Barbara
Wagner Middle School
Philadelphia, Pennsylvania

Rochford, Tracy
Louis Armstrong Middle School/IS 227
East Elmhurst, New York

Rodriguez, Ashley
John C. Martinez Junior High School
Parlier, California

Rowe, Michael
Washington Middle School
Long Beach, California

Sayles, Nichole
Hall McCarter Middle School
Blue Springs, Missouri

Schall, Harvest
Castle Rock Elementary School
Castella, California

Schellenberg, Katie
Corpus Christi School
Pacific Palisades, California

Schmees, Katherine
Milford Junior High School
Milford, Ohio

Schned, Paul
Richmond School
Hanover, New Hampshire

Schneider, Jennie
Parkway West Middle School
Chesterfield, Missouri

Scialanga, Michelle
Taylor Middle School
Millbrae, California

Shye, Kathryn
Happy Valley Elementary School
Anderson, California

Sirikulvadhana, Tiffany
Orange Grove Middle School
Hacienda Heights, California

Smetak, Laura
Orange Grove Middle School
Hacienda Heights, California

Smith, Shannon
Mary Putnam Henck Intermediate School
Lake Arrowhead, California

Smith-Paden, Patricia
Chappelow Middle School
Evans, Colorado

Sones, Mandy
Knox Junior High School
The Woodlands, Texas

Song, Sarah
Orange Grove Middle School
Hacienda Heights, California

Souza, Molly
Georgetown School
Georgetown, California

Stewart, Larry
Windsor Elementary School
Cincinnati, Ohio

Stites, Aaron
Redlands Middle School
Grand Junction, Colorado

Sturzione, James Van Duyn
Glen Rock Middle School
Glen Rock, New Jersey

Sundberg, Sarah
Milford Junior High School
Milford, Ohio

Swan, Tessa
Pacheco Elementary School
Redding, California

Swanson, Kurt
Allamuchy Elementary School
Allamuchy, New Jersey

Swihart, Bruce
Redlands Middle School
Grand Junction, Colorado

Syron, Christine
Nottingham Middle Community Education Center
St. Louis, Missouri

Taylor, Cody
Bella Vista Elementary School
Bella Vista, California

Thomas, Jennifer
Hoover Middle School
San Jose, California

Thompson, Robbie
Hefner Middle School
Oklahoma City, Oklahoma

Todd, Wanda
Hampton Middle School
Detroit, Michigan

Torning, Fraser
Allamuchy Elementary School
Allamuchy, New Jersey

Torres, Erica
Truman Middle School
Albuquerque, New Mexico

Tyroch, Melissa
Bonham Middle School
Temple, Texas

Ulibarri, Shavonne
John C. Martinez Junior High School
Parlier, California

Vanderham, Lynsey
Eagleview Middle School
Colorado Springs, Colorado

Vemula, Suni
Ada Junior High School
Ada, Oklahoma

Venable, Virginia
Chillicothe Junior High School
Chillicothe, Missouri

Vickers, Lori
Lake Braddock Secondary School
Springfield, Virginia

Vickers, Vanessa
Kings Glen School
Springfield, Virginia

Villanueva, Rene
John C. Martinez Junior High School
Parlier, California

Villasenor, Jose
Dana Middle School
San Pedro, California

Ward, Kimberly
Desert Horizon Elementary School
Phoenix, Arizona

Weeks, Josanna
Bellmont Middle School
Decatur, Indiana

West, Tyrel
Wheatland Junior High School
Wheatland, Wyoming

Whipple, Mike
Canandaigua Middle School
Canandaigua, New York

White, Schaefer
Richmond Middle School
Hanover, New Hampshire

Wilhelm, Paula
Wheatland Junior High School
Wheatland, Wyoming

Williams, Bonnie
Washburn School
Cincinnati, Ohio

Williams, Jason
Parkway West Middle School
Chesterfield, Missouri

Wiseman, Kristin
Glen Park Elementary School
New Berlin, Wisconsin

Wiseman, Megan
Glen Park Elementary School
New Berlin, Wisconsin

Yu, Veronica
Piñon Mesa Middle School
Victorville, California

Zipse, Elizabeth
Redlands Middle School
Grand Junction, Colorado

Acknowledgments (continued)

Delacorte Press/Seymour Lawrence, a division of Bantam Doubleday Dell Publishing Group, Inc.
"The Kid Nobody Could Handle," from *Welcome to the Monkey House* by Kurt Vonnegut, Jr. Copyright © 1961 by Kurt Vonnegut, Jr. Used by permission of Delacorte Press/Seymour Lawrence, a division of Bantam Doubleday Dell Publishing Group, Inc.

Harcourt Brace & Company
"For My Sister Molly Who in the Fifties" by Alice Walker, from *Revolutionary Petunias & Other Poems*, copyright © 1972 by Alice Walker. Reprinted by permission of Harcourt Brace & Company.

International Center of Photography
"The Gift" from *1992 Wall Calendar* created by the Creative Learning Community, East Harlem, with the International Center of Photography, New York, NY. Reprinted by permission.

Gish Jen
"The White Umbrella" by Gish Jen. Copyright 1984 by Gish Jen. First published in *The Yale Review*. Reprinted by permission of the author.

Norma Fox Mazer
"Calling Jack Kettle" is reprinted by permission of the author, Norma Fox Mazer. First appeared in *Scope Magazine*, volume 43, no. 13. Copyright 1995 by Norma Fox Mazer. All rights reserved.

N. Scott Momaday
"The Delight Song of the Tsoai-Talee" by N. Scott Momaday, published in *Carriers of the Dream Wheel*, edited by Duane Niatum.

New Moon Publishing, Inc.
Excerpt from "Dear Luna" (renamed "Dear Editor"), published in *New Moon: The Magazine For Girls and Their Dreams*, July/August 1995, is reprinted with permission from New Moon Publishing, P.O. Box 3587, Duluth, MN 55803. (218) 728-5507.

The New Yorker Magazine, Inc.
"Lego" by David Owen from *The Talk of the Town*, January 14, 1991. Reprinted by permission; © 1991 The New Yorker Magazine, Inc. All rights reserved.

Naomi Shihab Nye
"Famous" by Naomi Shihab Nye from *Hugging the Jukebox*. Copyright © 1982 by Naomi Shihab Nye. Reprinted by permission of the author.

Marian Reiner for the author
"The Possessors" from *The Sidewalk Racer and Other Poems of Sports and Motion* by Lillian Morrison. Copyright © 1965, 1967, 1968, 1977 by Lillian Morrison. Reprinted by permission of Marian Reiner for the author.

Simon & Schuster, Inc.
"The Old Grandfather and His Little Grandson" from *Twenty-Two Russian Tales for Young Children* by Leo Tolstoy. Copyright © 1969 by Miriam Morton. Reprinted by permission of Simon & Schuster, Inc.

Virginia Driving Hawk Sneve
"The Medicine Bag" by Virginia Driving Hawk Sneve, published in *Boy's Life*, March 1975. Reprinted by permission of the author.

The Estate of William Stafford
"The Osage Orange Tree" by William Stafford. Copyright © 1959 William Stafford, from *Oregon Centennial Anthology* (State Printing Section of Oregon). Reprinted by permission of The Estate of William Stafford.

Third Woman Press
"Good Hot Dogs" from *My Wicked Wicked Ways* by Sandra Cisneros. Copyright 1987 by Sandra Cisneros. Reprinted by permission of Third Woman Press, Berkeley, CA.

Christopher Thomas
"Untitled" by Christopher Thomas, published in *CSD III Review*, Community School District 3, 1995 Writing Project, New York, NY.

Note: Every effort has been made to locate the copyright owner of material reprinted in this book. Omissions brought to our attention will be corrected in subsequent printings.

Photo and Fine Arts Credits

Boldface numbers refer to the page on which the art is found.

Cover: Untitled, Che Chen, Walt Whitman High School, Bethesda, Mayland; **Kv:** *G-Clef: The Music and Me*, Michael Schwikardt, Artwork from the permanent collection of THIRTEEN/WNET's Student Arts Festival, 1978-1993; **Kvi:** *Me, Twice Lit in the Shadows*, Neng Her, The Scholastic Art & Writing Awards; **Kvii:** *On the Wheel*, Stratton Huggins, The Scholastic Art & Writing Awards; **Kviii:** *Remembrance (Erinnerung)*, ca. 1918, Marc Chagall, Gouache, Indian ink and pencil on paper 31.7 x 22.3 cm. Solomon R. Guggenheim Museum, New York, Gift, Solomon R. Guggenheim Museum, 1941, Photograph by David Heald © Solomon R. Guggenheim Foundation, New York (FN 41.440).; **Kix:** (bottom) Culver Pictures, Inc.; **Kx:** © Maldonado, Alexandra/SIS, New York; **K4:** Nicole Frosh; **K5:** Richard Hutchings /Photo Edit; **K6:** *Untitled, n.d.* Susan Kahn, oil on canvas, 20x24 (50.8x61.0) Unsigned, Gift of Dr. & Mrs. John J. McMullen, 87.2 Collection of the Montclair Art Museum; **K8:** David Young-Wolff/Photo Edit; **K10:** Chuck Savage/The Stock Market; **K11:** David Barnes/The Stock Market; **K13:** Courtesy of the author; **K15:** *G-Clef: The Music and Me*, Michael Schwikardt, Artwork from the permanent collection of THIRTEEN/WNET's Student Arts Festival, 1978-1993; **K16:** *Bear Lake, 1931*, Georgia O'Keeffe, oil on canvas 16 ¹/₂ x 36 ¹/₂ in. Museum of Fine Arts, Museum of New Mexico, Museum of New Mexico Foundation Collection; **K17:** Jeff Greenberg/Omni-Photo Communications, Inc.; **K18:** (background) Pete Saloutos/The Stock Market; (bottom) Arte Publico Press; **K20:** Perkins School for the Blind; **K21:** Reproduced from the Collections of the Library of Congress. LC-G9-Z1-137,816A; **K22, K23, K24** (center): Courtesy of the American Foundation for the Blind; **K24:** (background) Reproduced from the Collections of the Library of Congress. LC-G9-Z1-137,816A; **K26:** (left) Lawrence Migdale/Photo Researchers, Inc.; (center) *City Street, 1955*, David Park, oil on canvas, 59" x 45 ¹/₂", Howad S. Wilson Memorial Collection, Sheldon Memorial Art Gallery, University of Nebraska; **K27:** (bottom) William Johnson/Stock Boston; (right) Lawrence Migdale/Photo Researchers, Inc.; **K28** (left) Lawrence Migdale/Photo Researchers, Inc.; **K29** (right) Lawrence Migdale/Photo Researchers, Inc.; **K30** (left) Lawrence Migdale/Photo Researchers, Inc.; **K31:** (center) *Boy and Car, 1955*, David Park, oil on canvas, 18x24 inches, Salander O'Reilly Galleries. Private Collection, California; (right) Lawrence Migdale/Photo Researchers, Inc.; **K32–33:** Lawrence Migdale/Photo Researchers, Inc.; **K34:** (left) Lawrence Migdale/Photo Researchers, Inc.; **K34–35** (center) Tony Freeman/Photo Edit; **K35:** (right) Lawrence Migdale/Photo Researchers, Inc.; **K36:** (left) Lawrence Migdale/Photo Researchers, Inc.; **K37:** (center) Barrie Fanton/Omni-Photo Communications, Inc.; (right) Lawrence Migdale/Photo Researchers, Inc.; **K38** (left) Lawrence Migdale/Photo Researchers, Inc.; **K39:** (left) P. Prince/Gamma-Liaison; (right) Lawrence Migdale/Photo Researchers, Inc.; **K41:** *G-Clef: The Music and Me*, Michael Schwikardt, Artwork from the permanent collection of THIRTEEN/WNET's Student Arts Festival, 1978–1993; **K43:** Harold Ober Associates; **K44–45:** Audrey Gottlieb/Monkmeyer; **K47:** Jonathan Nourok/Photo Edit; **K48:** Courtesy of the artist; **K50:** Prentice Hall; **K52:** (right) Mel Digiacomo/IMAGE BANK; **K52-53:** (background) Rogers/Monkmeyer; **K54:** Richard Hutchings/Photo Researchers, Inc.; **K54–55,K56–57:** (background) Rogers/Monkmeyer; **K57:** (right) *Green Eyes, 1988* (detail), Stephen Scott Young, watercolor and drybrush on paper, 25 x 15 inches, Photography courtesy of John H. Surovek Gallery, Palm Beach, Florida; **K58:** & **K58–59:** (background) Rogers/Monkmeyer; **K59:** (center) © Nikky Finney; **K60:** (background) Rogers/Monkmeyer; **K61:** *Me, Twice Lit in the Shadows*, Neng Her, The Scholastic Art & Writing Awards; **K62:** *Remembrance (Erinnerung)*, ca. 1918, Marc Chagall, Gouache, Indian ink and pencil on paper 31.7 x 22.3 cm. Solomon R. Guggenheim Museum, New York, Gift, Solomon R. Guggenheim Museum, 1941, Photograph by David Heald © Solomon R. Guggenheim Foundation, New York (FN 41.440).; **K64:** (bottom) Culver Pictures, Inc.; **K66:** (bottom) Daemmrich/Stock Boston; **K66–67:** Roy Morsch/The Stock Market; **K68:** (background) Roy Morsch/The Stock Market; (left) Photo by Rubén Guzmán; **K69:** David Young-Wolff/Photo Edit; **K70** (top), (center), David Young-Wolff/Photo Edit; (bottom) Penni Gladstone/Outline; **K72:** Byron/Monkmeyer; **K75:** 3169(3)- Rawhide Shield with design of Sioux warrior, Cat. #50.1/ 2448, Courtesy Department of Library Services, American Museum of Natural History; **K76:** *Indian on* a Galloping Horse after Remington No.2, 1976, Fritz Scholder, Color lithograph, 30 x 22 1/4 in. Collection of the Museum of Fine Arts, Museum of New Mexico: Gift of Mr. and Mrs. Ben Q. Adams.; **K78:** Courtesy of the author.; **K80–81:** (background) Leonard Lee Rue, III/Photo Researchers, Inc.; **K81:** (center) Arnold Comes of Age (detail), 1930, Grant Wood, oil on panel, 27"x23" Nebraska Art Association, Courtesy of Sheldon Memorial Art Gallery, University of Nebraska-Lincoln ©1996 Estate of Grant Wood /Licensed by VAGA, New York, NY; **K82:** (center) Ice Glare, 1933, Charles Burchfield, watercolor on paper, 30 3/4" x 24 3/4". Collection of Whitney Museum of American Art, Purchase, 33.64. Copyright © 1995: Whitney Museum of American Art; **K82–83:** (background) Leonard Lee Rue, III/Photo Researchers, Inc.; **K83:** (center) Jim Harrison Gallery; **K84:** (top) The Hupper Farm 1939, N.C. Wyeth, egg tempera on panel, h: 24 3/4, w: 39 3/4" Dallas Museum of Art, Gift of C. R. Smith; **K84–85:** (background) Leonard Lee Rue, III/Photo Researchers, Inc.; **K85:** (bottom) Photo © 1991 by Dan Labby. Courtesy of Harper Collins.; **K86:** (background) Leonard Lee Rue, III/Photo Researchers, Inc.; **K87:** Me, Twice Lit in the Shadows, Neng Her, The Scholastic Art & Writing Awards; **K89:** Prentice Hall; **K90:** David Hoptman; **K92:** (center) La Guitare Noire, 1926, Juan Gris, oil on canvas, 19 3/4 x 28 5/8" The University of Iowa Museum of Art, Gift of Owen and Leone Elliott.; (bottom) Arte Publico Press; **K94:** Visa, 1951, Stuart Davis, oil on canvas, 40 x 52 inches (101.6 x 132.1 cm). The Museum of Modern Art, New York. Gift of Mrs. Gertrud A. Mellon. Photograph © 1995 The Museum of Modern Art, New York. ©1996 Estate of Stuart Davis/Licensed by VAGA, New York, NY; **K95:** Courtesy of the author; **K99:** On the Wheel, Stratton Huggins, The Scholastic Art & Writing Awards; **K100:** Plantations on the Mississippi River - map from Natchez to New Orleans, 1858 (Norman Chart) Historic New Orleans Collection, accession no. 1947.1 1-v; **K101:** Culver Pictures, Inc.; **K102:** from "The Book of the Great South" by Edward King, 1875. Photo by Silver Burdett Ginn; **K103:** Mark Twain House, Hartford, CT; **K104:** Courtesy of the Mariners Museum, Newport News VA; **K106:** Mark Twain Home and Museum; **K108:** Culver Pictures, Inc.; **K110:** Myrleen Ferguson Cate/Photo Edit; **K111:** (top) Myrleen Ferguson Cate/Photo Edit; (bottom) Courtesy of the author. Photo by Michael Nye; **K112:** The Granger Collection, New York; **K114:** Photo by Silver Burdett Ginn; **K114–115:** (background) Russell Thompson/Omni-Photo Communications, Inc.; **K115:** (center) Photofest; **K116:** Bror Karlsson/Omni-Photo Communications, Inc.; **K118-119:** (background) James Marshall/The Stock Market; **K121:** Photo by Silver Burdett Ginn; **K122:** (tl) & (tc) Friends and Alumni of LaGuardia High School; (right) Addison-Wesley; (bc), M. Dycke Ferrigno. Photo by Avery Willard; (bl) M. Dycke Ferrigno; **K124, K126:** Courtesy of Lego; **K127:** Villard Books, Photo by Jim Paisley; **K129:** On the Wheel, Stratton Huggins, The Scholastic Art & Writing Awards; **K133:** David W. Hamilton/IMAGE BANK; **K138:** (tr) Harry Snaveley; (bl) From FLOWERS FOR ALGERNON by Daniel Keyes. Used by permission of Bantam Doubleday Dell Publishing Group, Inc.; (br) From CHILDREN OF THE RIVER by Linda Crew. Copyright (c) 1989 by Linda Crew. Used by permission of Dell Books, a division of Bantam Doubleday Dell Publishing Group, Inc. **K139:** (tl) From WHEN LEGENDS DIE by Hal Borland. Used by permission of Bantam Doubleday Dell Publishing Group, Inc.; (bl) Penguin Books.

Commissioned Illustrations

K102, K103, K125: Carol Richman

Electronic Page Makeup

Larry Rosenthal, Tom Tedesco, Dawn Annunziata, Penny Baker, Betsy Bostwick, Maude Davis, Paul DelSignore, Irene Ehrmann, Jacob Farah, Alison Grabow, Gregory Harrison, Jr., Marnie Ingman, Laura Maggio, Lynn Mandarino, David Rosenthal, Mitchell Rosenthal, Rasul Sharif, Scott Steinhardt

Administrative Services

Diane Gerard

Photo Research Service

Omni-Photo Communications, Inc.